ANTENNAS F...

by

IAN POOLE, B.Sc.(Eng.), C.Eng., M.I.E.E.

BERNARD BABANI (publishing) LTD
THE GRAMPIANS
SHEPHERDS BUSH ROAD
LONDON W6 7NF
ENGLAND

Please Note

Although every care has been taken with the production of this book to ensure that any projects, designs, modifications and/or programs, etc., contained herewith, operate in a correct and safe manner and also that any components specified are normally available in Great Britain, the Publishers do not accept responsibility in any way for the failure, including fault in design, of any project, design, modification or program to work correctly, or to cause damage to any other equipment that it may be connected to or used in conjunction with, or in respect of any other damage or injury that may be so caused, nor do the Publishers accept responsibility in any way for the failure to obtain specified components.

Notice is also given that if equipment that is still under warranty is modified in any way or used or connected with home-built equipment then that warranty may be void.

© 1994 BERNARD BABANI (publishing) LTD

First Published — March 1994

British Library Cataloguing in Publication Data
Poole, I. D.
    Antennas for VHF and UHF
    I. Title
    621.3824

    ISBN 0 85934 246 8

Printed and Bound in Great Britain by Cox & Wyman Ltd, Reading

Preface

The subject of aerials is a fascinating one. It covers many areas of electronics from the practical to the theoretical, from receiving to transmitting and from low frequencies to very high ones.

Aerials are very important for any receiver or transmitter. The performance of the whole system is often governed or limited by that of the aerial. For example no matter how good a hi-fi tuner, it cannot achieve its ultimate performance when connected to a poor aerial. The same is true for short wave listeners because a poor aerial will not enable them to receive the weaker and more interesting signals. The performance of an aerial becomes even more important when transmitters are being used. Here the difference between a good and a poor aerial becomes even more striking.

The performance of an aerial depends upon a number of factors. Firstly the design of the aerial must be suitable for its use. It must also be constructed well, particularly if it is to be used outside when it must be able to withstand the forces of the wind as well as the effects of corrosion from the rain and gasses in the air. Often an aerial can perform very well when it is first put up. However after a few months or years its performance can slowly deteriorate. Sometimes this can go unnoticed because of the rate at which it happens but still have a large effect on the aerial's performance. Finally the aerial must be erected correctly. Not only must it be fitted up so that it will not fall down, but it must also be sited in the best position to enable it to pick up or transmit the best signal.

This book has been written to give a general background to the operation of antennas. It also describes a number of aerials which are suitable for operation in the VHF and UHF portions of the spectrum.

Ian Poole

Other Titles of Interest

Note

The terms Antenna and Aerial now seem to be regarded in this country as being totally interchangeable. Also the convention seems to be to use antennas as plural and not as might be expected antennae which only apply to the insect world.

Contents

Chapter 1

BASIC CONCEPTS

The theory behind the operation of aerials can be very complex involving long and complicated mathematics. Accordingly many people choose to ignore it, resorting to purely experimental methods. However to obtain the best results from any antenna design it is best to have some knowledge about the basic concepts and theory behind its operation. This does not necessarily involve any significant amount of mathematics because a qualitative approach can often be quite adequate for most experimenters. In order to do this the first place to start is by looking at the nature of radio or electromagnetic waves themselves.

Electromagnetic Waves
The purpose of an aerial is either to receive or transmit radio signals. Like light and ultraviolet rays, radio waves are electromagnetic (or E/M) waves. These waves are made up from two constituents: an electric field and a magnetic field which are inseparable from one another. As shown in Figure 1.1 they are at right angles to one another, and it can also be seen that when the magnetic wave is at its peak the electric field is at its minimum and vice versa. In fact it is because of this interchange between the two types of field that its energy is never zero and accordingly it can propagate over considerable distances.

To gain more of an idea of how the wave travels it can be likened in some ways to the action of the surface of a pond when a stone is dropped into the water. The ripples spread out all around, decreasing in amplitude as they travel outwards. So it is with an electromagnetic wave although its action is somewhat more complicated.

There are a number of points which can be noted about electromagnetic waves. The first is the wavelength. This is the distance between the same point on two successive waves. Normally the crest is chosen as a good example to visualize although any point can be chosen. This may vary in length

1

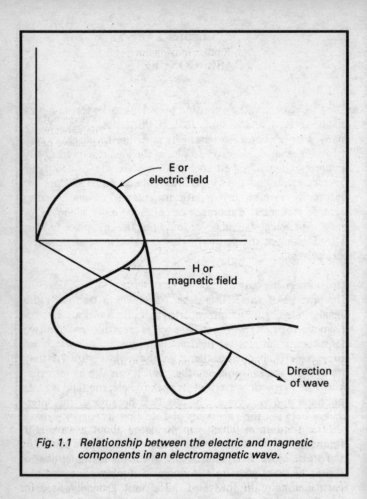

Fig. 1.1 *Relationship between the electric and magnetic components in an electromagnetic wave.*

from many hundreds or thousands of metres to lengths shorter than a millimetre.

Another feature which can be noted about an electromagnetic wave is its speed. Being the same as a light wave it has the same speed. Normally this is taken to be 3×10^8 metres a second or more exactly 299 792 500 metres a second in a vacuum.

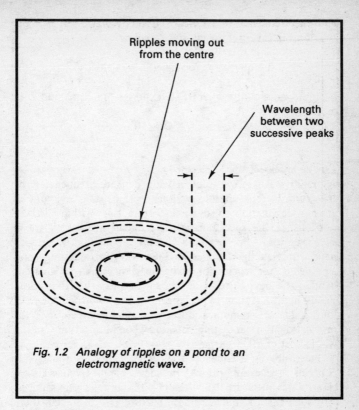

Ripples moving out from the centre

Wavelength between two successive peaks

Fig. 1.2 Analogy of ripples on a pond to an electromagnetic wave.

The third facet which can be noted about a wave is its frequency of vibration. In the analogy of the ripple caused by the stone being dropped into the pond this is the number of times the wave goes up and down in a given time and at a particular point in the pond. The unit generally used for frequency is the hertz and this corresponds to one cycle or wave per second. As frequencies which are encountered can be very high the standard prefixes of kilo (kilohertz, kHz) for a thousand hertz, Mega (Megahertz, MHz) for a million hertz, and Giga (Gigahertz, GHz) for a thousand million hertz are commonly used.

It can probably also be seen that there must be some form of mathematical relationship between the wavelength, velocity,

3

and the frequency of an electromagnetic wave. In fact the relationship is very simple as shown below:

$$Frequency \times Wavelength = Velocity$$

or more commonly where F is expressed in hertz and λ in metres:

$$F \times \lambda = 3 \times 10^8$$

Frequency Spectrum

As radio waves cover such a wide band of frequencies the spectrum is split up into various sections and each one is given a designation as shown in Figure 1.3. Within all these portions of the spectrum lie the familiar ones which are in everyday use. For example the MF or medium frequency band contains the familiar medium wave broadcasting band as well as frequencies for maritime services and an amateur band. The next portion of the spectrum is the HF section. Bands in this section of the spectrum are renowned for their long distance communications and as such they are used for international broadcasting, amateur communications and a whole host of other purposes.

Increasing in frequency the VHF section is found. It contains services like the FM Broadcast band as well as allocations which were used for the old 405 line television services. Although these frequencies have been re-used in the UK there are still a large number of countries in Europe which continue to use them for television. In addition to broadcasting there are also bands for amateurs, private mobile communications, aircraft, and a host of other users.

Moving up in frequency again the next portion of the spectrum is the UHF band. Here the 625 line TV transmissions can be found as well as many other services like the cellular telephones, amateurs, and so forth.

The frequency spectrum goes much further up in frequency and there are many other types of use for it. One of these is satellite communications including the new direct broadcast satellite services. Land based point to point services also use up a large part of the spectrum.

4

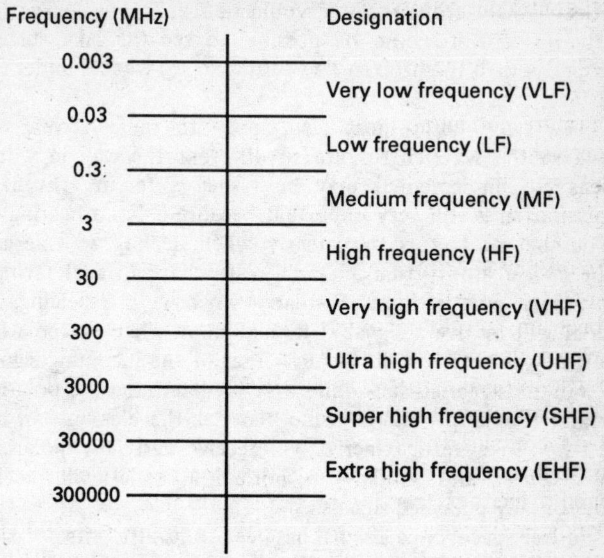

Frequency (MHz)	Designation
0.003	Very low frequency (VLF)
0.03	Low frequency (LF)
0.3	Medium frequency (MF)
3	High frequency (HF)
30	Very high frequency (VHF)
300	Ultra high frequency (UHF)
3000	Super high frequency (SHF)
30000	Extra high frequency (EHF)
300000	

Fig. 1.3 The frequency spectrum.

Polarisation

It is a well known fact that light waves can be polarised. Very basically this means that the vibrations occur in a particular plane. One analogy for this could be seen when a piece of string is made to vibrate. If it only vibrated up and down then it would be said to be vertically polarised. As an electromagnetic wave has two constituents the polarisation is taken to be that of the electric field.

In fact the most common example of polarisation of an electromagnetic wave is seen with light waves. Polaroid sunglasses and lenses for cameras are seen everywhere when the sun is out. They only let light with a particular polarisation through. As light which has been reflected off a surface like water will be mainly polarised in one direction, a Polaroid material can be used to reduce the reflections. Thus if the sun was shining onto the surface of a lake, normally only the reflected light from the sun would be seen. However with a Polaroid lens it would be possible to see the lake surface properly, or it might even be possible to see what is under the surface.

The same basic ideas also apply to radio waves, but because the wavelengths are so different the way in which ideas are implemented may be rather different. Even so polarisation is still very important because it has a bearing on a number of factors particularly when dealing with aerials. The main reason is that an aerial will radiate a signal having a particular polarisation. Similarly when it is receiving, an aerial will receive a signal at its maximum when the polarisation of the aerial is the same as that of the incoming signal.

For most aerials it is quite easy to determine the polarisation. It is simply in the same plane as the elements of the aerial. So a vertical aerial will receive vertically polarised signals best and similarly a horizontal aerial will receive horizontally polarised signals.

In free space, once a signal has been transmitted its polarisation will remain the same. So in order to receive the maximum signal both transmitting and receiving aerials must be in the same plane. If for any reason their polarisations are at ninety degrees to one another (i.e. cross polarised) then in theory no signal would be received.

For real applications on earth it is found that once a signal has been transmitted then its polarisation will remain broadly the same. However reflections from objects in the path can change the polarisation, and as the received signal will be the sum of the direct signal plus a number of reflected signals the overall polarisation of the signal can change slightly.

One everyday visual example of the fact that transmitting and receiving aerials should be the same can be seen on most houses today. It will be noticed that all the TV aerials directed at a given TV transmitting aerial will have the same polarisation. In general they are horizontally polarised if it is a main transmitter or vertically polarised if it is a relay station.

The Aerial System

A complete aerial system is made up from more than just the

aerial element itself, although this is obviously the central part of the whole setup. In addition there are other items like the feeder which is used to transfer the energy from the transmitter to the aerial, or in the case of a receiving system it is used to transfer the energy from the aerial to the receiver input. Feeders are needed as the optimum situation for the aerial is seldom at the same place as the equipment.

Other items are also needed. Often an item known as a balun may be needed or possibly some other network could be used to match impedances. All of these items form part of the whole aerial system.

Operation of an Aerial

The actual way in which an aerial operates is quite complicated if a full understanding is needed. Fortunately it is possible to attempt a simple explanation to give a broad qualitative understanding of its function. Essentially there is a current flowing in the aerial and this generates the magnetic part of the electromagnetic wave. The electric constituent is generated by the varying charge.

It is also interesting to note that close to the aerial there is also an inductive field the same as that in a transformer. This is not part of the electromagnetic wave, but it can distort measurements close to the aerial. It can also mean that transmitting aerials are more likely to cause interference when they are close to other aerials or wiring that might have the signal induced into them. Receiving aerials are more susceptible to interference if they are close to house wiring and the like. Fortunately this inductive field falls away fairly rapidly and it is barely detectable beyond about two or three wavelengths.

Resonance

An aerial is essentially a form of tuned circuit, and as such it exhibits the same properties. It has a complex impedance. Below its resonant frequency it is capacitive and above the resonant frequency it becomes inductive. When an aerial is resonant the inductive and capacitive components cancel one another out and the aerial becomes purely resistive.

Virtually all VHF and UHF types of aerial are operated so that the aerial element itself is at resonance. This means that the feeder should see a purely resistive load.

Radiation Resistance

In any circuit which uses an alternating current there must be a resistance present for any power to be dissipated. If a load is purely inductive or capacitive then no power will be dissipated. The same is true for aerials, but when power is actually radiated it is lost just as if a resistor were present. In fact a signal generator connected to the aerial would see the same as if a resistive load was present and its value can be calculated using Ohm's law. With this in mind it is convenient to look upon this resistance as a "radiation resistance". In fact most aerials will be designed to have a specific radiation resistance. The most common values are 75 ohms for television and broadcast FM, and 50 ohms for other uses.

The value of the resistance is important for an aerial system to operate efficiently. In order to obtain the maximum power transfer from the aerial to the receiver or from the transmitter to the aerial both should have the same resistance.

If an aerial is operating correctly it will appear as a pure resistance. If, for example it was not on its resonant frequency then it would appear as a resistor in series with either a capacitor or inductor. In order to bring the circuit back to its peak efficiency an equal and opposite reactance must be added by using an inductor or capacitor so that the aerial appears purely resistive again.

The radiation resistance of a system can be calculated quite simply by applying Ohm's Law. The resistance can be found by dividing the voltage by the current at the feed point.

Directivity

The radiation from a practical aerial is not the same in all directions. In fact the intensity of the radiation will vary around the aerial from place to place and a plot of the pattern of this radiation is called a polar diagram. Essentially this plots a curve around an aerial showing the intensity of the radiation at each point. An example for an aerial known as a dipole is shown in Figure 1.4.

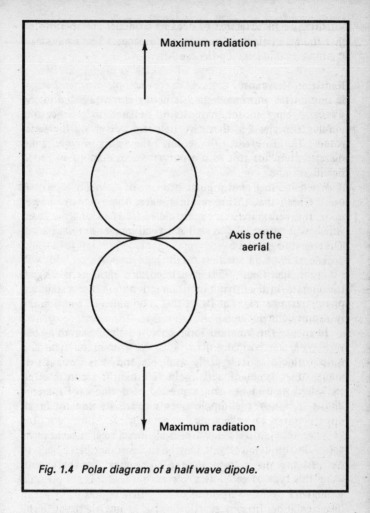

↑ Maximum radiation

Axis of the aerial

↓ Maximum radiation

Fig. 1.4 Polar diagram of a half wave dipole.

The radiation pattern of an aerial is very important. In order to make the best use of the transmitter power it is necessary to ensure it is all directed to the areas where the receiving stations are likely to be. For example if all the receiving stations are located in one direction away from the transmitter then it is useless to transmit power in any other direction. One example of needing to direct the transmitted power in a particular direction could occur when a broadcast transmitter is located by the sea.

Another major advantage of making an aerial directive is that it will have some gain. Take the example of when a signal is transmitted from an aerial. If power is not radiated in one direction then it will have to be radiated in another one making the signal in that direction stronger giving the aerial some gain. In effect this "beams" the signal in a particular direction and for this reason directive aerials are often called beams.

When looking at the polar diagram of a directive aerial it will be seen that there are areas where there is more power than in others. These areas are called lobes. Usually a beam will have a major lobe as well as several smaller or minor lobes as shown in Figure 1.5.

The gain of an aerial is often quite important and it will often be specified. This is defined as a ratio of the signal transmitted in the "maximum" direction to that of a standard or reference aerial. The figure that is obtained is then normally expressed in decibels.

In theory the standard aerial could be almost anything but two types are normally used. The most common type is a simple dipole as it is easily available and it is the basis of many other types of aerial. In this case the gain is often expressed as dBd i.e. gain expressed in decibels (dB) over a dipole. However a dipole does not radiate equally in all directions and so a theoretical aerial called an isotropic source i.e. one that radiates equally in all directions, is sometimes used. In this case the gain may be specified in dBi, i.e. gain in decibels over an isotropic source. The main drawback with using this type of aerial as a reference is that it is not possible to make a perfect version of one, so that figures using it can only really be theoretical. However it is possible to relate the two gains as a dipole has a gain of 2.1 dB over an isotropic source, i.e. 2.1 dBi.

Apart from the forward gain of an aerial another parameter which is important is the front to back ratio. This will be expressed in decibels and as the name implies it is the ratio of the signal in the forward direction to the signal in the

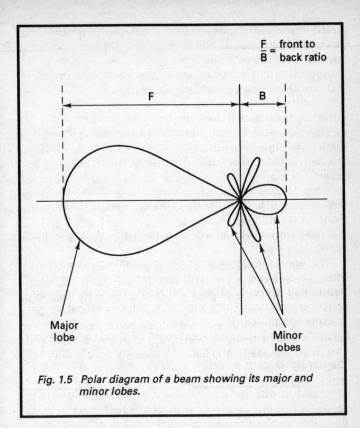

$\dfrac{F}{B} = $ front to back ratio

F

B

Major lobe

Minor lobes

Fig. 1.5 Polar diagram of a beam showing its major and minor lobes.

opposite direction or as it is sometimes called off the back of the beam. This can be important if interference is being caused by signals in the opposite direction to the wanted one. It is sometimes important to know whether maximum forward gain or the best front to back ratio is required because the two do not always coincide.

So far all the reasoning about directivity in aerials has applied to the case when an aerial is used for transmitting. The same reasoning can also be applied when an aerial is used for receiving and the aerial will be able to pick up signals in one direction better than another, and better than an aerial with no directivity. This has two effects. The first is that any interfering signals coming in from a different direction to the wanted one can be reduced in strength, and the second is that the aerial gain can be used to increase the strength of the wanted signal. This can be particularly useful when trying to receive signals which are of marginal strength.

Angle of Radiation
Another aspect of the directivity is associated with what is called the angle of radiation. Essentially this is the radiation pattern in the vertical plane. An aerial is said to have a low angle of radiation if the main lobe of the signal is close to the ground. Conversely an aerial with a high angle of radiation will have much of its power directed upwards. For most VHF and UHF aerials it is necessary to have a low angle of radiation. An example of a typical radiation pattern is shown in Figure 1.6.

The angle of radiation is determined by two main factors. The first is obviously the aerial itself. Some aerials will be able to concentrate more of their power at a low angle because of their directive nature. A basic horizontal aerial with little or no directivity, such as a dipole will not be very good. A beam aerial will be a lot better. Vertical aerials are generally good because the maximum radiation is at nearly right angles to the axis of the aerial.

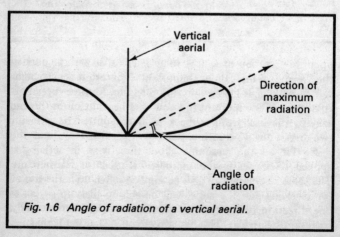

Fig. 1.6 Angle of radiation of a vertical aerial.

The other factor which determines the angle of radiation of an aerial is its height above ground. Reflections from the ground can combine with the signal directly from the aerial. Dependent upon the height above ground this can either reinforce or reduce the low angle signal. It is found that the optimum height above ground for the best low angle performance is a multiple of half wavelengths.

Bandwidth

It has already been mentioned that an aerial will have a resonant frequency, and like any other form of tuned circuit it will have a certain bandwidth over which it can operate. This bandwidth can be rather vaguely defined as the frequency range over which it will give satisfactory service. This definition has to be rather vague because there are a number of different features of the aerial's performance which will vary with frequency. Some of these may not be particularly important in some instances, whereas others may be.

One major feature of an aerial which does change with frequency is its impedance. This in turn can cause the amount of reflected power to increase. If the aerial is used for transmitting it may be that beyond a given level of reflected power damage may be caused to either the transmitter or the feeder, and this is quite likely to be a factor which limits the operating bandwidth of an aerial. As far as receiving is concerned, the impedance changes of the aerial are not as critical as they will mean that the signal transfer from the aerial itself to the feeder is reduced and in turn the efficiency will fall.

Another feature of aerials which changes with frequency is the directional pattern. In the case of a beam it is particularly noticeable. In particular the front to back ratio will fall off rapidly outside a given bandwidth, and in addition to this the overall directional pattern will change. If this is a major feature of the design it is possible that this may limit the bandwidth.

In order to increase the bandwidth of an aerial there are a number of measures which can be taken. One is the use of thicker conductors. Another is the actual type of aerial used. For example a folded dipole which is described fully in Chapter 3 has a wider bandwidth than a non-folded one.

In fact looking at a standard television aerial it is possible to see both of these features included.

Chapter 2

FEEDERS

The feeder is an essential part of any aerial system. It serves to transfer the energy picked up by the aerial down to the receiver or conversely it transfers the power from the transmitter to the aerial. This has to be done with the minimum amount of power loss. Also the lengths of feeder can be fairly long in some instances. This is because the optimum position for an aerial is generally as high as possible and away from objects which are likely to act as a screen. This means that it will be some distance away from the equipment connected to it. In view of this the feeder plays an important role in the overall operation of the aerial. A poor feeder will result in the whole aerial system being degraded. Conversely a good feeder will ensure that the maximum amount of energy is transferred from the aerial to the receiver, or from the transmitter to the aerial.

The operation of a feeder is not quite as straightforward as one might expect from the first look. There are several parameters and characteristics which feeders possess. These play a vital role in the operation of the feeder and need to be understood, at least in general.

Characteristic Impedance
The first aspect of a feeder is its impedance. Just as an aerial has a value of impedance, and a receiver or transmitter has an input or output impedance, so a feeder has what is called its characteristic impedance. This impedance is very important because it is necessary to match the feeder impedance to that of the rest of the system.

The impedance of the feeder is governed by a number of factors. The physical dimensions of the feeder have a very large bearing on it. Also the dielectric constant of the material between and sometimes around the feeder can vary the impedance. Fortunately it is relatively easy to control these factors to a sufficient degree to make feeders with the right value of impedance.

The impedance of the feeder is very important. In order to achieve the optimum efficiency in an aerial system the aerial, the feeder and the transmitter or receiver should all have the same impedance, or have a matching network to ensure that they are all matched. The reason for this is that in any system the maximum power transfer takes place when the impedance of the source and the load are the same. If there is what is called a mismatch between the two then the efficiency is reduced.

Standing Waves

When a load is perfectly matched to the impedance of the feeder the voltage and current will be constant along the feeder as shown in Figure 2.1. However when a load is not

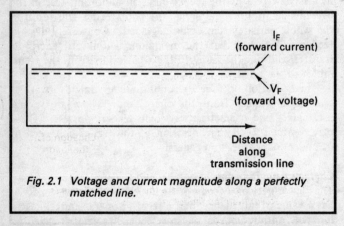

I_F
(forward current)

V_F
(forward voltage)

Distance
along
transmission line

Fig. 2.1   Voltage and current magnitude along a perfectly matched line.

matched the situation is a little different. It has already been mentioned that for maximum power transfer the impedance of the source and load must be the same. When looking at the transfer of the power from the feeder to the load the feeder acts as the source. In this case the power enters the feeder and travels along it. If there is a poor match between the feeder and the load then only a proportion of the power can be transferred. The remaining power cannot disappear and is reflected back along the feeder towards the source. When this happens the voltages and currents associated with the forward and the reflected power add and subtract in diffferent places. The net result of this is that standing waves are set up and points of high and low current and voltage are seen.

As an example, Figure 2.2 shows a feeder which is terminated by a load with a resistance lower than the characteristic impedance of the feeder. At the point of the load the voltage

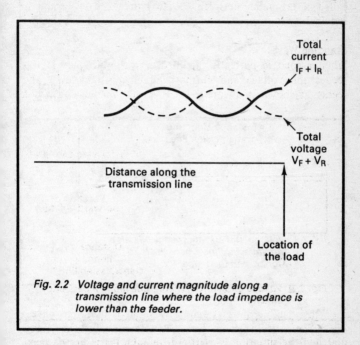

Fig. 2.2   Voltage and current magnitude along a
transmission line where the load impedance is
lower than the feeder.

is lower than if it had been a perfect match whilst the current is higher. Further back down the feeder the voltage and current changes. At a point an eighth of a wavelength away from the load the current is falling whilst the voltage is rising. Then a quarter of a wavelength away from the load the voltage has reached its maximum whilst the current has reached its minimum. This logic can be followed through until at a point half a wavelength away from the load the current and voltage are the same as at the load.

Similarly if the load resistance was higher than the characteristic impedance of the feeder the current at the point of the load would be lower than had it been perfectly terminated. Again standing waves would be set up but the patterns would be those shown in Figure 2.3.

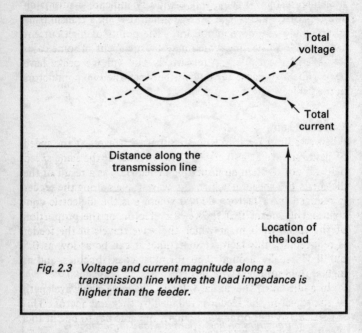

Fig. 2.3 *Voltage and current magnitude along a transmission line where the load impedance is higher than the feeder.*

When talking about standing waves it is useful to have a way of quantifying them. Generally a factor called the "standing wave ratio" or SWR is used. It is the ratio of the maximum to minimum values on the line. Most often the voltage standing wave ratio or VSWR is used.

The standing wave ratio is also linked to the proportion of power which is reflected. This is generally called the reflection coefficient (ρ). The link between the two is quite easy to work out because the maximum of the standing wave will be the forward power (P) plus the reflected power, i.e. $P(1 + \rho)$ and the minimum will be the forward power minus the reflected power, i.e. $P(1 - \rho)$. This means that the ratio of the two becomes:

$$SWR = \frac{(1 + \rho)}{(1 - \rho)}$$

The standing waves in themselves will not be a problem in a receiving system. They will obviously indicate a mismatch and loss of efficiency but no more than this. In a transmitting system they are more important. The points of high current can cause local heating which may be sufficient in some cases to deform the cable. Alternatively the voltage peaks have been known to cause breakdown between the two conductors in the cable.

Velocity Factor
When a radio wave travels in free space it travels at the speed of light. It would also travel along a feeder at the same speed if it did not contain an insulating dielectric. As a result of the dielectric the speed at which the wave travels along the feeder is reduced by a factor of $1/\sqrt{\epsilon}$ where ϵ is the dielectric constant. This means that the velocity factor, or the proportion of the speed of light at which the wave travels in the feeder is reduced by this factor. Sometimes it can be as low as 0.5 but it is usually around 0.66 for most coaxial cables, and as high as 0.98 for open wire feeders.

In addition to the actual velocity changing, the wavelength of the signal in the feeder is reduced by the same factor. This is particularly important if a length of cable has to be cut to a specific number of wavelengths.

Loss
Apart from figures like the characteristic impedance and velocity factor of a cable the loss is another very important factor. Obviously in an ideal world it would be possible to feed a certain amount of power into the cable at one end and expect to see the same amount at the other end. However in reality this is never the case. Each cable will have a certain amount of loss and this will be dependent on the length. Normally this is expressed as a certain number of decibels over a certain length.

This loss is caused by a number of factors. One is the actual resistance of the wire. This can be reduced by making the wires thicker but this in turn means that the whole cable has to be made larger if the same impedance is to be maintained. This obviously puts up the cost. Another reason for power being lost is that it can be dissipated in the dielectric material between the two conductors. Normally this will be quite low. But if for any reason moisture has crept into the dielectric then the loss will rise quite dramatically. As a result of this it is necessary to ensure that the outer sleeve on any coax is intact and that the ends are sealed.

The loss of a cable is also dependent upon the frequency in use. It will rise as the frequency is increased. Accordingly the loss of a given cable will be given at a number of different frequencies, and an intelligent guess or interpolation can be made for the particular frequency in use.

The amount of loss a cable has is of paramount importance in any aerial system particularly when it comes to very sensitive receiver systems capable of picking up signals close to the noise level. In these circumstances any signal which is lost cannot be regained by adding more amplification as the associated noise will be amplified as well.

Types of Feeder
There are a number of different types of feeder which can be used. Some are in common everyday use whilst others are seen only very occasionally. Each one has its own advantages and disadvantages, and applications to which it is best suited. Often the choice of which type of feeder is quite easy, but it is useful to know exactly what is available and so three of the more commonly used types are outlined here.

Coax
The most common type of feeder used today is undoubtedly coaxial feeder or coax. It is used for television down leads as well as being used in the majority of other aerial installations at VHF and UHF frequencies.

As the name suggests the cable consists of two concentric conductors as shown in Figure 2.4. The centre conductor will usually be made of copper. Sometimes it may be a single

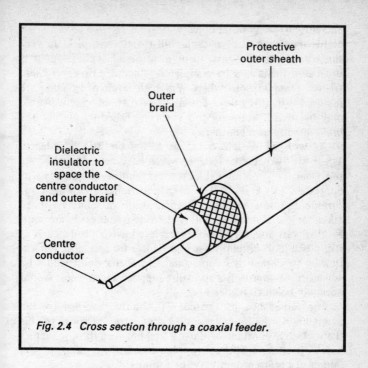

Fig. 2.4 Cross section through a coaxial feeder.

Protective outer sheath

Outer braid

Dielectric insulator to space the centre conductor and outer braid

Centre conductor

conductor whilst at other times it may consist of several strands. The outer conductor is normally made up from a copper braid. This enables the cable to be flexible which would not be the case if the outer conductor was solid. Between the two conductors there is an insulating dielectric. This holds the two conductors apart and in an ideal world would not introduce any loss. In turn there is a final cover or outer sheath. This serves no electrical function, but gives a vital protection needed to prevent dirt and moisture attacking the cable.

The cable carries current in both the inner and the outer conductors, but because they are equal and opposite all the fields are confined to within the cable and it does not radiate or pick up signals. As there are no fields outside the cable it is not affected by nearby objects. This means it is ideal for applications where the cable has to be taken through the house and close to many other objects.

In practice a coaxial cable will radiate and pick up very small amounts of signal. For most aerial applications it is sufficiently small to be completely ignored. However there are some applications where very high levels of isolation are required. In this case a double or even triple screened cable may be used. Normally this is accomplished by placing one braid directly over another.

As with all feeders coax has a characteristic impedance. There are two standard values which have been adopted over the years. 75 ohm cable is used almost exclusively for domestic TV and VHF FM applications. However for commercial, amateur and CB applications 50 ohms has been taken as the standard. Whilst these two standards are used for the vast majority of coax cable which is produced it is still possible to obtain other impedances for specialist applications. To obtain these non-standard impedances it would be necessary to approach a specialist supplier and the cost would normally be much higher.

The impedance of the coax is chiefly governed by the diameters of the inner and outer conductors. On top of this the dielectric constant of the material between the conductors has a bearing. The relationship needed to calculate the impedance is given simply by the formula:

$$Z_0 = \frac{138}{\sqrt{\epsilon}} \log \left(\frac{D}{d} \right)$$

where D is the inner diameter of the outer conductor and d is the diameter of the inner conductor.

Open Wire Feeder

Rather than having two concentric conductors to contain the fields associated with a radio frequency signal it is also possible to use two parallel conductors as in Figure 2.5. This type of cable is known as a ribbon or "twin" feeder. Sometimes where the two cables are kept apart at intervals by spacers the feeder is called open wire feeder, but this is normally only used at frequencies below about 30 MHz. It works because it

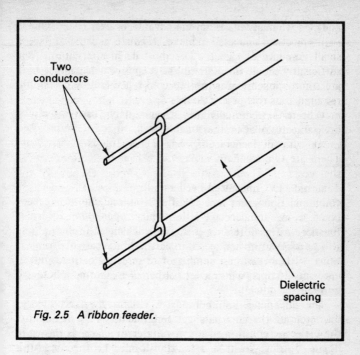

Fig. 2.5 A ribbon feeder.

does not allow any signal to radiate if the conductors are close together (less than 0.01 wavelengths spacing for most applications) because the fields from both the conductors will be equal and opposite and cancel one another out. The advantage of this type of cable is that at lower frequencies it can be made to have a loss which is much less than coax. However as the frequency rises and the required spacing falls it does not become a practicable type of feeder and it is not normally used above frequencies of about 150 MHz.

The impedance of the feeder can be calculated from the formula:

$$Z_0 = \frac{276}{\sqrt{\epsilon}} \log\left(\frac{D}{d}\right)$$

where D is the distance between the conductors and d is the diameter of the conductors.

23

Open wire feeder has several advantages over coax. One is that it is cheap and easy to make. However because of its loss at VHF and UHF it is very seldom used. In addition to this it can easily become unbalanced and its performance impaired if it is taken close to other objects, and it is therefore unsuitable for cable runs within a house.

Despite these disadvantages it can often be used in temporary aerial installations reasonably well. It can be improvised by the use of the white lighting flex as this is a fairly close approximation to 75 ohm feeder.

Balanced and Unbalanced Feeders
Coax and open wire feeders differ from one another because coax is an unbalanced feeder whilst open wire feeder is balanced. The difference is that an unbalanced feeder has one of the conductors connected to earth. In the case of coax it is obvious that the outer conductor or screen is earthed, but in the case of open wire feeder neither of its two conductors is earthed.

This difference is quite important because a balanced feeder can be used to feed a balanced aerial such as a dipole directly. However coax will need a transformer or balun as shown in Figure 2.6. This will be a 1:1 transformer, i.e. the same turns

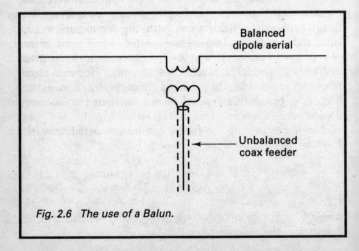

Fig. 2.6   The use of a Balun.

24

on each winding if the impedance of the aerial and feeder are the same. It can also be used for matching the aerial and feeder if the impedances are different. This is accomplished by having a different number of turns in the primary and secondary and using it as an impedance transformer. The impedance and turns ratio of the transformer or balun are related by the formula:

$$\frac{N1}{N2} = \sqrt{\frac{Z1}{Z2}}$$

Whilst it is possible to operate balanced aerials from a coaxial feeder without a balun and many people perceive little deterioration in their performance, there are some penalties to not using them when they are needed. The main one is that the feeder will start to pick up and radiate signals. In turn this can lead to poor or noisy reception or if a transmitter is being used then not all the power will be radiated from the aerial.

Waveguide

The third type of feeder is known as waveguide. It consists of a hollow metal "pipe". Usually it is rectangular as shown in Figure 2.7 but it is possible to have a circular waveguide as well. It is different to other forms of feeder in that it does not have conventional conductors carrying equal and opposite currents as in the case of coax or open wire feeder. Instead it has an electromagnetic wave travelling inside it, the waveguide acting as an enclosure preventing any energy from escaping.

A signal can be introduced into a waveguide in a number of ways. One is to use an item known as a launcher like the one shown in Figure 2.8. In this a small probe which may be the centre conductor of some coax extends slightly into the waveguide. It is orientated so that it is parallel to the electric field which needs to be set up. Any signal from the coax will then be launched into the waveguide. An alternative method is to use a small loop which encompasses the magnetic lines of force. However the most common method is to use the open circuit probe.

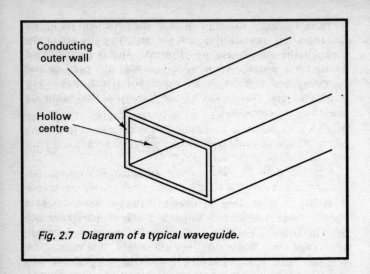

Fig. 2.7 Diagram of a typical waveguide.

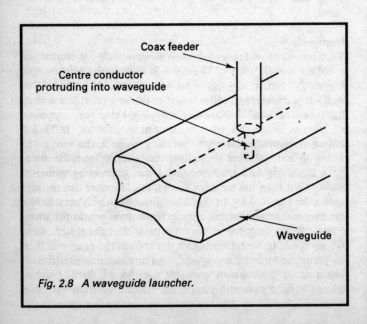

Fig. 2.8 A waveguide launcher.

These launchers not only enable signals to be transmitted into the waveguide but they can also be used to pick signals up as well. Alternatively the signal can be radiated or picked up directly from the end of the waveguide. In fact an unterminated waveguide will radiate its signal perfectly well although its directional properties will not be particularly good for most purposes. In view of this fact it is very important that one NEVER looks down a waveguide that is connected to a transmitter because it could be radiating energy of a sufficient level to cause damage to the eyes.

It is found that a waveguide of particular dimensions cannot operate below a certain frequency called its cutoff frequency. Below this no signals propagate down it. This means that a number of different sizes of waveguide are available dependent upon what frequency or band is in use. These sizes are standardized and allocated numbers in the form WG**. As an example, a waveguide for use between 2.60 and 3.96 GHz has internal dimensions of 72 × 34 mm and it is given the designation WG10.

The main advantage of waveguide is its low loss at high frequencies when compared to coax. It becomes a viable alternative for some systems above frequencies of 2 − 3 GHz. As an example, WG10 made from aluminium has a loss of 0.7dB per 30 metres. Coax for use at these frequencies would have a very much higher level of attenuation. Against this the cost of waveguide is very much higher and as a result it is generally only used in professional applications.

Coax Cable Specifications

Although it is possible to go into the local TV or radio shop and buy standard or low loss coax cable, when using cable for amateur or commercial applications it is more usual to buy coax with a specific type number. Coax with a type number will have a certain specification. Its dimensions, impedance, loss, velocity factor and so forth will all be defined even though the manufacturer may not be known.

Two main systems are in use. One originated in the United Kingdom and its type numbers all start with UR. The other system is American with type numbers commencing with the letters RG. As the two systems are different but cover very

Fig. 2.9 Coax Cable Specifications

Type	*Characteristic Impedance*	*Outside Diameter*	*Velocity Factor*	*Attenuation (dB/10 metres) @ 100 MHz*	*Attenuation (dB/10 metres) @ 1000 MHz*	*Comments*
RG5/U	52.5	8.4	0.66	1.0	3.8	
RG6A/U	75	8.4	0.66	1.0	3.7	
RG9/U	51.0	10.7	0.66	0.66	2.4	
RG10A/U	50	12.1	0.66	0.66	2.6	
RG11A/U	75	10.3	0.66	0.76	2.6	
RG12A/U	75	12.1	0.66	0.76	2.6	
RG20A/U	50	30.4	0.66	0.22	1.2	
RG58C/U	50	5.0	0.66	1.8	7.6	
RG59B/U	75	6.1	0.66	1.2	4.6	
RG62A/U	93	6.1	0.84	0.9	2.8	
RG213/U	50	10.3	0.66	0.62	2.6	Polythene dielectric
RG214/U	50	10.8	0.66	0.76	2.9	Double screened Silver plated copper wire
RG223/U	50	5.5	0.66	1.58	5.4	
UR43	50	5	0.66	1.3	4.46	
UR57	75	10.2	0.66	0.63	2.3	Similar to RG11A/U
UR67	50	10.3	0.66	0.66	2.52	Similar to RG213/U
UR74	51	22.1	0.66	0.33	1.4	
UR76	51	5.0	0.66	1.7	7.3	Similar to RG58C/U
UR77	75	22.1	0.66	0.33	1.4	
UR79	50	21.7	0.96	0.17	0.6	
UR90	75	6.1	0.66	1.2	4.1	Similar to RG59B/U
*Std TV Coax	75	5.1	0.66	1.1	4.0	
*Low Loss TV Coax	75	7.25	0.86	0.75	2.6	Semi-air spaced

*These cables are not standardized. Figures given are typical only.

similar items there are a number of cables which are very similar and alternatives exist between the two systems. A list of the more commonly used cables is shown in Figure 2.9.

Connectors
There is a very wide variety of connectors which are in use today. Some connectors are more familiar than others. Some are used for their high frequency capability, whilst others have gained their popularity for their low cost. In any case it is necessary to know what connectors are available and what their relative merits and shortcomings are.

One of the most widely used connectors is the standard TV or Belling Lee connector shown in Figure 2.10(a). It is almost universally used for domestic television in the United Kingdom because it is very cheap. Whilst it is acceptable for internal television use it should not be used for any application where the specification is of importance. It should also not be used externally because it is made of aluminium and this will corrode quite quickly.

The "UHF" connector is shown in Figure 2.10(b). Often the plug is referred to as a PL259 and the socket as an SO239. It is widely used in amateur radio applications and some video systems. They have a screw fixing to prevent accidental disconnection. The basic connector is designed for use with thick cables so when they are used with thinner cables a reducer has to be used. In terms of their performance they do not possess a constant impedance, i.e. its characteristic impedance changes across the length of the connector. This is not a problem in the HF portion of the frequency spectrum but it means that they can really only be used up to frequencies of about 500 MHz even if high quality versions are purchased. Their use is generally not recommended on the 70 centimetre amateur band. Additionally some of the cheap versions will have an inferior performance and will become quite lossy in the VHF portion of the frequency spectrum.

A BNC connector is shown in Figure 2.10(c). It is widely used in professional circles being used on most oscilloscopes and many other laboratory instruments. It has a bayonet fixing to prevent accidental disconnection whilst being easy to disconnect when necessary. Electrically it is designed to

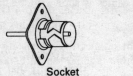

Socket　　　　　　　　Plug

Fig. 2.10a "Belling Lee" type socket and plug.

Plug
PL259

Socket
(SO239)

Fig. 2.10b UHF series plug and socket.

Plug　　　　　　　　Socket

Fig. 2.10c BNC plug and socket.

Plug　　　　　　　　Socket

Fig. 2.10d TNC plug and socket.

Socket

Plug

Fig. 2.10e N type plug and socket.

present a constant impedance and it is most common in its 50 ohm version, although 75 ohm ones can be obtained. It is recommended for operation at frequencies up to 4 GHz and it can be used up to 10 GHz provided the top quality versions are obtained.

The TNC connector shown in Figure 2.10(d) is very similar to the BNC connector. The main difference is that it has a screw fitting instead of the bayonet one. The frequency limit is also slightly better than that of the BNC with special versions being able to be used up to 18 GHz.

Another type of connector used in professional circles and favoured by many radio amateurs is the N connector shown in Figure 2.10(e). It is a high quality constant impedance connector which is capable of operation up to 10 GHz. It is also suitable for high power operation and dependent upon the particular version it can take larger diameter cables.

Chapter 3

THE DIPOLE

The dipole is probably the most important type of aerial. Although it is not commonly used at VHF and UHF on its own, it is used as the basic element in the vast majority of aerials today. It is found in TV and VHF FM aerials not to mention those used in a whole host of other applications.

Even in its basic form a dipole can provide quite satisfactory service, providing the solution to a number of aerial requirements. It is simple and easy to construct, and where gain or directivity are not particularly important it can often be the ideal solution.

Basic Dipole

A basic dipole consists of a length of wire cut in the middle and having the two ends connected to the feeder as shown in Figure 3.1. For normal operation the aerial can be any number of electrical half wavelengths long. However for VHF and UHF operation a single half wavelength is almost invariably used.

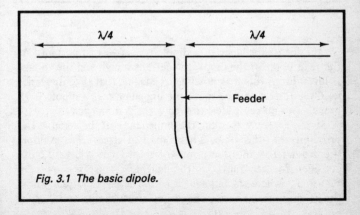

Fig. 3.1 The basic dipole.

Current Voltage and Feed Impedance

The current distribution along a dipole is roughly sinusoidal. It falls to zero at the end and is at a maximum in the middle. Conversely the voltage is low at the middle and rises to a maximum at the ends as shown in Figure 3.2. Although a dipole which is just one half wavelength long is the most common sort, dipoles which are other multiples of wavelength are also sometimes used, which may have different current and voltage distributions. For example a dipole of three half wavelengths.

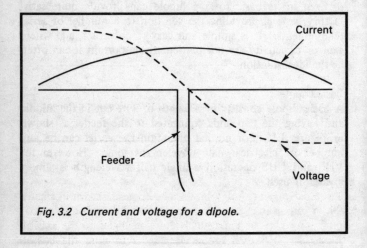

Fig. 3.2 Current and voltage for a dipole.

The feed impedance of a dipole is also very important. At the feed point of the dipole the current is high and the voltage is low. From this it is possible to imagine that the impedance is low. In fact in free space the impedance of a dipole is 78 ohms. This makes it ideal to feed with 75 ohm coax.

It is very easy to alter the impedance of an aerial. The proximity of other objects has a marked effect. For example the ground has an effect, and the impedance will vary quite considerably according to the height. This is shown by Figure 3.3 where the impedance of the aerial is plotted against the height in terms of the operational wavelength.

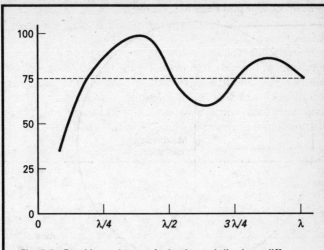

Fig. 3.3 Feed impedance of a horizontal dipole at different heights.

Radiation Pattern

The polar diagram for a half wave dipole is shown in Figure 3.4. From this it can be seen that the direction of maximum sensitivity or radiation is at right angles to the axis of the aerial. It is then found to fall to zero along the axis of the aerial. However if the length of the aerial is changed then this pattern is altered. As the length of the aerial is extended then lobes develope. There are main lobes which tend to move towards the axis of the aerial as well as a number of minor ones.

Folded Dipole

In its basic form a dipole will consist of a single wire or conductor cut in the middle to accommodate the feeder. It has already been seen that the feed impedance can be altered by the proximity of other objects. When the dipole forms part of a larger aerial such as the Yagi described in Chapter 5 its

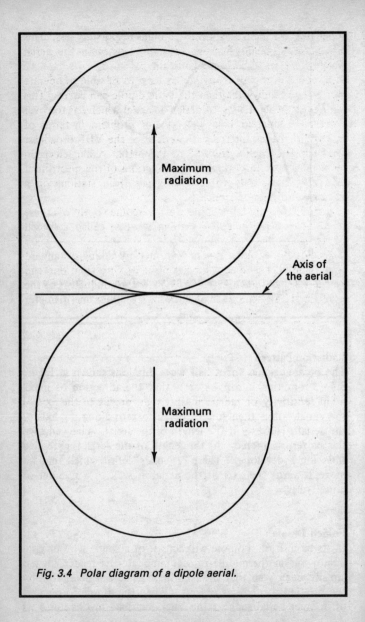

Fig. 3.4 Polar diagram of a dipole aerial.

impedance can fall to as low as 10 ohms or possibly less. This can cause problems because resistance losses in the aerial system can start to become significant.

In addition to this many aerials have to be able to operate over larger bandwidths than the basic dipole can cover. This can happen when trying to design an aerial which has to cover a complete amateur band. A greater problem in terms of bandwidth is encountered with aerials for the VHF broadcast band which stretches from 88 to 108 MHz. Again television aerials also have to cover very wide sections of the spectrum if they are to be able to receive signals from stations on a number of different channels.

Fortunately it is possible to overcome both of these problems at least in part by using what is called a folded dipole.

Essentially a folded dipole is formed by taking a standard dipole and then adding a further piece of wire from one end to the other as shown in Figure 3.5. If the conductors of the basic dipole and the added section are of the same diameter

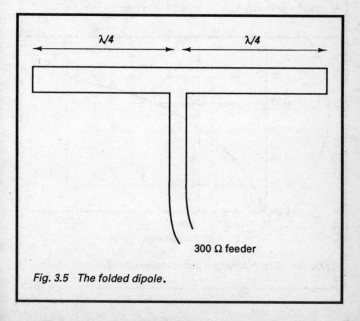

Fig. 3.5 The folded dipole.

then it is found that the impedance of the aerial is raised by a factor of 4. By changing the ratios of the diameters of the two conductors the impedance can be changed. This means that it is possible to obtain an almost exact match for most requirements. However for most applications where the conductor diameter is constant the impedance of a folded dipole is taken to be 300 ohms.

Length

The length of a dipole is quite critical as the aerial is a resonant circuit. However its length will not be an exact multiple of half wavelengths. There are a number of reasons for this and it means that an aerial will be slightly shorter than the length calculated for a wave travelling in free space.

For a half wave dipole the length for a wave travelling in free space is calculated and this is multiplied by a factor "A". For aerials in the VHF and UHF portions of the factor is generally about 0.96. It is mainly dependent upon the ratio of the length of the aerial to the thickness of the wire or tube. A graph showing this relationship is given in Figure 3.6.

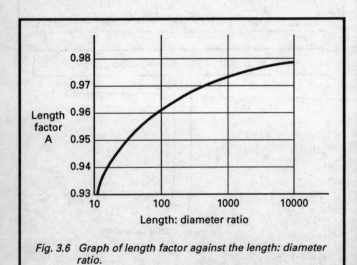

Fig. 3.6 Graph of length factor against the length: diameter ratio.

In order to calculate the length of a half wave dipole the simple formulae given below can be used:

$$\text{length (metres)} = \frac{150 \times A}{\text{frequency in MHz}}$$

$$\text{length (inches)} = \frac{5905 \times A}{\text{frequency in MHz}}$$

Using these formulae it is possible to calculate the length of a half wave dipole, however as a starting point a table of lengths for a number of bands is given in Figure 3.7. Even though these lengths are normally quite repeatable it is always best to make any aerial slightly longer than the calculations might indicate. This needs to be done because changes in the thickness of wire being used, etc., may alter the length slightly. Once the aerial wire has been cut to length it is possible to trim it so that it resonates exactly on the right frequency. It is best to trim the aerial length in fairly small steps because the wire cannot be replaced very easily once it has been cut.

Fig. 3.7 Table of Half Wave Dipole Lengths

Band/Frequency	Nominal Length	
	Inches	*cms*
88 – 108 MHz (VHF FM Broadcast Band)	59	150
130 MHz	42	107
144 – 146 MHz (2 Metre Amateur Band)	38	96.5
430 – 440 MHz (70 cms Amateur Band)	12.5	31.75

Wire used 24/0.2 mm

Construction

The construction of a dipole is easy. Most of the details will depend upon its use, where it is to be placed and the materials available for its construction. The dipole may be made simply from ordinary wire or it may be made from tubing of one form or another. The overall length must be determined and then having cut this length it must be split in the middle for the feeder, one conductor from each leg of the aerial being connected to one conductor in the feeder.

As the voltage points of the aerial are at the ends care should be taken to ensure that they are kept away from nearby conductive objects. This is because they will tend to de-tune the aerial and can drastically reduce the signal. However the centre of the dipole is far less sensitive.

One very simple way of making up a dipole with its feeder for experimental or temporary use is with some of the white low current mains flex. When used as a feeder for radio frequency signals this type of wire is a reasonably close approximation to 75 ohm twin or open wire feeder. Another alternative to this is speaker wire used for car radios, etc. This can be used if the white mains flex is not available.

To make up the dipole the cable should have the two insulated wires split back away from one another and opened out as shown in Figure 3.8. The centre should then be secured to prevent the cable opening out any further. One method of

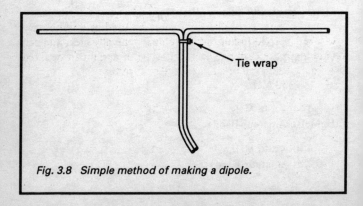

Fig. 3.8 Simple method of making a dipole.

doing this is to use a tie wrap such as those available from most electronics components stockists. The length of wire which has not been split can then be used as the feeder.

VHF FM Folded Dipole

Many hi-fi tuners have a 300 ohm input as well as the standard 75 ohm one. This input will normally have screw terminals although they will sometimes have a special 300 ohm connector. This input is ideal for use with a folded dipole which can be made up very simply. It requires only the use of a length of 300 ohm ribbon cable (not the computer multi-stranded ribbon cable) which can be bought from most electronic component stockists.

The first stage is to cut a length slightly longer than that required for the dipole element. At either end the centre plastic should be cut back and the remaining wire on either side stripped and joined together as shown in Figure 3.9. This should be done make sure that the overall length of the element is correct.

The next stage is to cut the bottom wire in the centre. The wires should be stripped back so that a second length of ribbon can be attached as shown. This can be made any suitable length, bearing in mind that it is likely to introduce a reasonable amount of loss if it is run within the house close to other objects. This enables the 300 ohm ribbon to be used as feeder to be connected. This may be any suitable length.

This cheap and easy VHF FM aerial is suitable for areas with high signal strengths, or it may be used as a temporary measure. The 300 ohm ribbon cable is generally clear and can be hidden quite easily. Often this type of aerial can be fixed behind a curtain rail or a large piece of furniture.

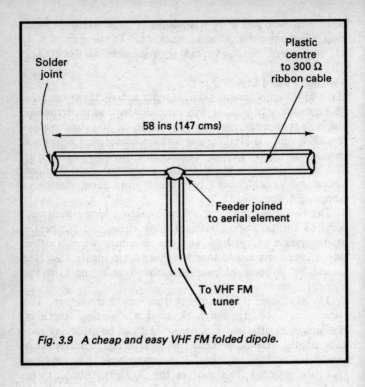

Solder joint

Plastic centre to 300 Ω ribbon cable

← 58 ins (147 cms) →

Feeder joined to aerial element

To VHF FM tuner

Fig. 3.9 A cheap and easy VHF FM folded dipole.

Chapter 4

THE YAGI

The Yagi is undoubtedly the most common form of "beam" or directive aerial in use today. It is used for virtually all TV aerials (with the exception of some of the small set top loops), external hi-fi aerials, and a large proportion of the aerials used by radio amateurs at these frequencies. In fact the Yagi is very effective whilst being relatively easy to construct and sturdy enough to withstand the rigours of the weather.

The name for the aerial may seem rather unusual. The full name for it is the Yagi-Uda. It was derived from the names of its two Japanese inventors Yagi and his student Uda. The aerial itself was first outlined in a paper which Yagi himself presented in 1928. Since then its use has grown rapidly to the stage where today a television aerial is synonymous with an aerial having a central boom with lots of elements attached.

The Aerial Itself

The Yagi has a dipole as its fundamental component. To this further "parasitic" elements are added. They are called parasitic elements because they are not directly connected to the coax feeder. Instead they operate by picking up power from the dipole and then using it to affect the properties of the whole aerial.

It is found that the amplitude and phase of the current which is induced in these elements is dependent upon their length and the spacing between them and the dipole or driven element.

If the parasitic element is made inductive it will be found that the induced currents are in such a phase that they reflect the power. This causes the aerial to radiate power more in one direction than another. An element which does this is called a reflector. It can be made inductive by tuning it below reasonance. This can be done by physically adding more inductance to the element in the form of a coil, or more commonly by making it about 5% longer than the

43

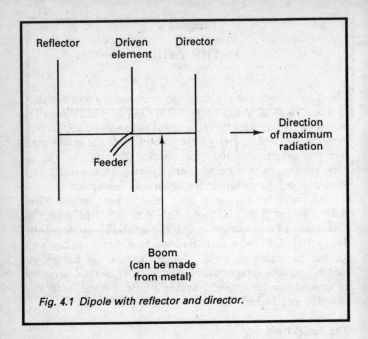

Fig. 4.1 Dipole with reflector and director.

driven element. The reflector is added to the aerial as shown in Figure 4.1.

If the parasitic element is made capacitive it will be found that the induced currents are in such a phase that they direct the power radiated by the whole aerial in the direction of the parasitic element. An element which does this is called a director. It can be made capacitive by tuning it above resonance. This can be done by physically adding some capacitance to the element in the form of a capacitor, or more commonly by making it about 5% shorter than the driven element. A director is added to the aerial as shown in Figure 4.1.

It is found that to increase the effect of beaming the power in a certain direction further directors can be added. However it is found that additional reflectors have no noticeable effect and only one reflector is ever used. A typical example of a Yagi using a reflector and several directors is shown in Figure 4.2.

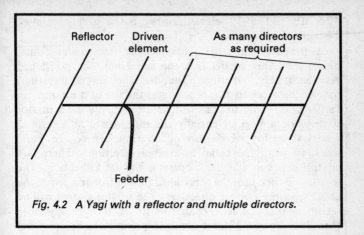

Fig. 4.2 A Yagi with a reflector and multiple directors.

Labels in figure: Reflector, Driven element, As many directors as required, Feeder

Gain

The gain of a Yagi depends primarily upon the number of elements which the aerial has. However the spacing between the element also has an effect. In terms of gain it is found that the spacing is not particularly critical. Provided that approximately the correct spacing is chosen adjustments will only make changes to the gain of a fraction of a decibel. For most purposes the spacing will be somewhere in the region of 0.15 to 0.3 of a wavelength.

The gain will obviously vary slightly from one aerial to another dependent upon a number of factors. However a two element design will give a maximum of around 5 dB gain over a dipole. If a director is added a total gain of around 7 dB can be obtained. Additional directors will give further gain. The actual amount will depend upon how many directors are used. Obviously the more directors the greater the gain. However the amount of gain an additional director will give depends upon how many are there already. If there are only a few then an extra one will give more than if there are a lot. A four element aerial will have a gain of up to about 9 dB so the second director has added about 2 dB gain, but as a rule of thumb each director will add about 1 dB. For example an 11 element array has a maximum gain of about

13.5 dB and a 12 element array has a gain of around 14.5 dB.

As the gain of the aerial is increased the beamwidth becomes narrower. This means that the aerial must be positioned very accurately. In turn if stations from several directions have to be received this necessitates the use of a rotator. In fact amateur radio stations will almost certainly use a rotator if they use a Yagi. Generally the rotator will be a form of electrical motor which can be controlled from the radio shack to point the aerial in a given direction. There is a control unit into which the operator will set a direction. The motor will then turn the aerial until the control unit senses the aerial is in the correct direction. The rotator system will be set up so that the aerial cannot be turned through any more than 360 degrees. This is done to prevent the feeder being wrapped around the mast.

When looking at the gain of the aerial it is also necessary to consider the front to back ratio. It can be seen from the typical polar diagram for a Yagi shown in Figure 4.3 there is a significant lobe from the back of the aerial. It is not possible to obtain a null here because the Yagi uses parasitic elements. If it used two driven elements it would be possible to obtain a null by adjusting the relative phases of the two elements. Even so it should be possible to obtain a front to back ratio of 10 dB or so on a Yagi.

Feed Impedance

Apart from altering the gain the element spacing alters the feed impedance of the aerial. In fact it has a far greater effect on this than the gain for most instances. By altering the spacing it is possible to ensure that a good match is achieved between the feeder and the aerial itself.

It is found that for a two element Yagi consisting of a driven element plus a reflector the feed impedance is about 50 ohms if the spacing is just over 0.2 wavelengths, whilst a 75 ohm match is achieved for a spacing of just under 0.3 wavelengths. Below a spacing of 0.2 wavelengths the impedance falls away rapidly and it can drop to 5 ohms or less for a spacing of 0.1 wavelengths. The resistance peaks at around 90 ohms for a spacing of about 0.5 wavelengths.

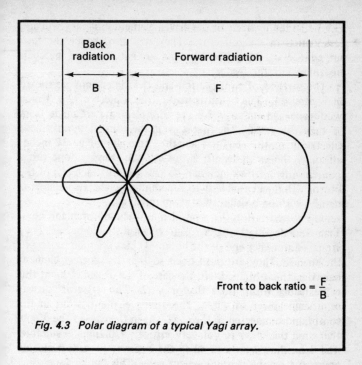

Fig. 4.3 Polar diagram of a typical Yagi array.

Within the diagram:

Back radiation

Forward radiation

B

F

Front to back ratio = $\dfrac{F}{B}$

The addition of further elements complicates the issue considerably but generally the impedance will be reduced. In any case a certain amount of experimentation is needed to perfect the design.

Many Yagi designs employ comparatively close spacings between the elements to keep the boom length within reasonable limits. In order to overcome the reduction in feed impedance which this causes a folded dipole driven element is usually used. This has the added benefit that the bandwidth is increased.

VHF FM Yagi For Indoor Use

A Yagi for VHF FM reception suitable for mounting inside the roof space can be made up very easily and cheaply from a few oddments of wood and wire. The design given here is for two elements, a driven element and a reflector. Directors can be added in front of the driven element, but they will add less gain than the reflector. They will also reduce the feed impedance of the driven element so that a poorer match is obtained with the feeder.

The method of construction and the dimensions are shown in Figure 4.4. The boom is made from a piece of 2 × 1 inch wood and the supports for the wire elements are made from ½ × ½ inch wood. The first stage in the construction is to cut the boom to the required length. This should be 32 inches although the exact length is not critical. Having done this a section ½ × ½ of an inch can be taken out of each end of the boom. This will enable it to accommodate the two elements rigidly, with no possibility of them moving.

The supports for the wire elements should be made next. Two 65 inch lengths of ½ × ½ inch wood should be cut. They are fixed to either end of the boom. U pins are then pinned to the wood. They are positioned so that the correct element length can be obtained. In the case of the driven element this is 59 inches whilst the reflector is 62. The reflector consists of a single piece of wire. The driven element is cut in the centre and connected to the coax. As in the case of the dipole the wire thickness is not very critical; 7/0.2mm is suitable. The coax should be secured to the boom to prevent it placing any strain on the driven element wire. This can be done using a tie wrap around the boom, or simply using a U pin. If a pin is used then care should be taken not to damage the coax.

The aerial has been tuned for the lower end of the VHF FM band. Whilst it will operate over the whole band it can be optimised for other sections if required. This is done by shortening the element lengths slightly.

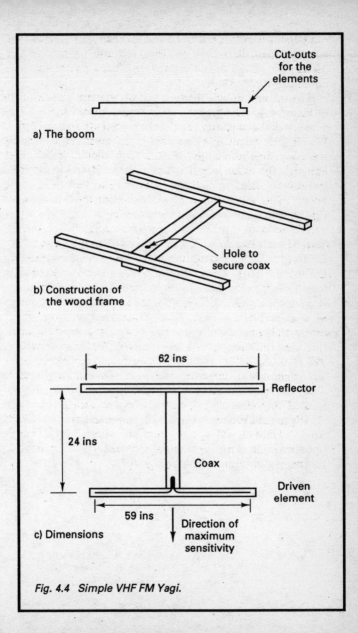

Cut-outs for the elements

a) The boom

Hole to secure coax

b) Construction of the wood frame

62 ins

Reflector

24 ins

Coax

Driven element

59 ins

Direction of maximum sensitivity

c) Dimensions

Fig. 4.4 Simple VHF FM Yagi.

Chapter 5

THE CUBICAL QUAD

The cubical quad or quad for short is not commonly used outside amateur radio circles. Here it found favour particularly amongst those addicts devoted to operation on the higher HF bands of 10, 15, and 20 metres. It was also fairly popular for use on 2 metres. However its lack of use outside the field of amateur radio does not mean that it has little to offer. On the contrary it can be a very useful aerial and it can give a very good account of itself.

The Quad Antenna

The basic quad element consists of a loop of wire a wavelength long arranged in the form of a square. As with the Yagi parasitic elements can be added to make the aerial more directional as shown in Figure 5.1. A reflector can be added behind the driven element. It is made inductive by tuning it below resonance. This can be done in a number of ways. The first is to make the reflector about 5% longer than the driven element. However this is not always the best way from a mechanical point of view because all the elements have to be made different sizes. A more elegant way is to keep the reflector the same physical size but add inductance in the form of a short circuited stub. Similarly directors can be made shorter or they can use open circuited stubs to tune them above resonance and make them capacitive.

The operation and development of the element can be seen in Figure 5.2. The first stage is to have two dipoles stacked above one another and fed in phase. This arrangement in itself gives a certain amount of gain because of the phasing effect between the two dipoles. The next stage is to retain the two separate dipoles but bend the ends together. It will be found that the voltages at the ends of the aerials will be in phase with one another. As a result it is possible to connect these ends together and remove one of the feeders.

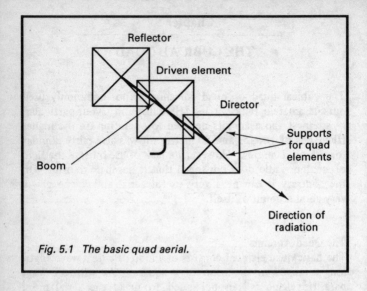

Reflector

Driven element

Director

Supports
for quad
elements

Boom

Direction of
radiation

Fig. 5.1   The basic quad aerial.

Current and Voltage Waveforms

From the development of the basic quad element it is fairly
easy to deduce where the current and voltage maxima will be.
As the current maximum is at the feed point the same is also
true for the quad. There is also another current maximum on
the opposite side of the loop to the feed point, i.e. where the
second feed point was. The voltage maxima appear at points
a quarter of a wavelength away from the feed point, i.e. where
the two ends of the dipole would have been. In view of the
position of the voltage points it is advisable not to position
any fixings at these points.

Element Spacing

In the same way that the element spacing played a large part
in the design of the Yagi, the same is found for the quad. In
general a spacing of around 0.15 to 0.2 of a wavelength is
used. This conveniently gives a feed impedance of around
50 ohms. If a two element quad has a spacing of just
over a quarter of a wavelength then the feed impedance rises
to around 75 ohms. This is convenient for designs used for

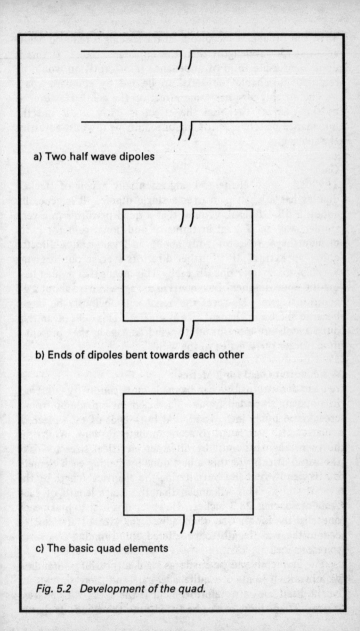

a) Two half wave dipoles

b) Ends of dipoles bent towards each other

c) The basic quad elements

Fig. 5.2 Development of the quad.

VHF FM broadcast reception. If the spacing is reduced below about 0.15 wavelengths then the impedance falls. If this is done then some form of impedance transformation would be required to enable the aerial to be fed by standard coax.

The spacing also has some effect on the gain. However as in the case of the Yagi the effect is fairly small and the impedance matching is the major requirement whilst adjusting the spacing.

Gain

The basic quad element, being essentially a pair of stacked dipoles has a slight gain over a single dipole. It is generally about 2 dB. It is also found that a quad performs in a very similar way to a Yagi in terms of additional gain for extra elements. A reflector adds about 5dB gain and a director about an extra 2 dB. Further directors average out at giving very approximately one dB each. This means that a quad having the same number of elements as a Yagi will have about 2 dB additional gain. However the aerial will obviously be larger because the basic element size is greater. This does mean that quad aerials are more prone to wind damage as they present a much larger surface area to the wind.

A 3 Element Quad for 2 Metres

A quad for internal use can be made quite simply by constructing a simple wooden frame. Each element is made up from a cross of ½ by ½ inch wood. At both ends of each piece of wood a small slot is cut to accommodate the wire. Whilst the different elements must be different electrical sizes to make the aerial directional this is best done by making each element the same physical size but altering the electrical length by the use of stubs. This will mean that the exact length of each cross member is 28.3 inches. However it is best to make each one slightly longer and then adjust the size of the slot to enable the wire length to be altered for trimming the aerial to resonance.

The frame should be made as rigid as possible. Standard woodworking joints are quite adequate and there should not be the need for extra reinforcement if the aerial is to be used inside. Then the wire can be fitted onto the wood. It should be as thick as reasonably possible to maintain a reasonable bandwidth. Twelve or 14 s.w.g. is quite suitable. The open end can then be terminated using a terminal block. This provides a method of keeping the aerial wire in place as well as a method of connecting the coax.

Each element is made the same. However instead of attaching coax the reflector and director use a stub instead. This should consist of a pair of lengths of wire about three inches long. One wire is attached in place of each of the coax connections. In the case of the reflector the stub is short circuited, whereas the stub for the director is left open circuit.

The boom for the aerial is made out of two lengths of 1 × 1 inch wood. They are mounted as shown in Figure 5.3. If necessary the spacing of the parasitic elements can be adjusted with these two lengths of wood acting as a clamp. However once all the adjustments have been made then all the elements should be firmly screwed and glued to the boom.

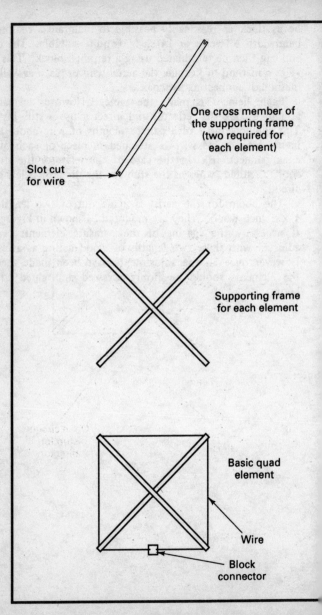

One cross member of
the supporting frame
(two required for
each element)

Slot cut
for wire

Supporting frame
for each element

Basic quad
element

Wire

Block
connector

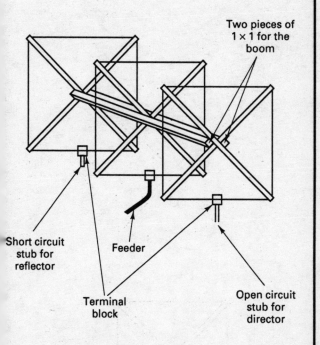

Two pieces of
1 × 1 for the
boom

Short circuit
stub for
reflector

Feeder

Terminal
block

Open circuit
stub for
director

Fig. 5.3   Construction of a 2 metre quad.

57

Chapter 6

VERTICAL AERIALS

Vertical aerials find widespread use in the VHF and UHF portions of the spectrum. One only has to look at the aerials which are used on cars to see this. Private mobile radio (PMR), cell phones, amateur radio and a number of other users all employ vertical aerials particularly for mobile communications. The reason for this widespread use is the omni-directional radiation pattern which they give in the horizontal plane. This means that the aerials do not have to be re-orientated to keep the signals constant as the car moves.

Although vertical aerials find widespread use on cars they are used in many other situations as well. In fact they are used in any application which needs a non-directional aerial.

There are several different types of vertical. The quarter wavelength aerial is the most basic form. There are a number of other different types which have their own advantages. One enhancement to the basic quarter wave aerial is made by extending its length. By doing this it is possible to concentrate more of the power into a lower angle of radiation. This is a distant advantage because any power which is radiated at a high angle is lost. In fact one popular form of vertical is the five eighths wavelength vertical. Another method of having a low angle of radiation is to have a number of different radiating elements above one another. If they are fed in the correct phase then the aerial can be made to have quite a significant gain over a standard quarter wave vertical. Even so the starting point for most verticals is the quarter wavelength aerial.

Quarter Wave Vertical

Like the name suggests the basic quarter wave vertical is based around a quarter wavelength vertical element as shown in Figure 6.1. The voltage and current waveforms show that at the end the voltage rises to a maximum whereas the current falls to a minimum. Then at the base of the aerial at the feed point, the voltage is at a minimum and the current is at its

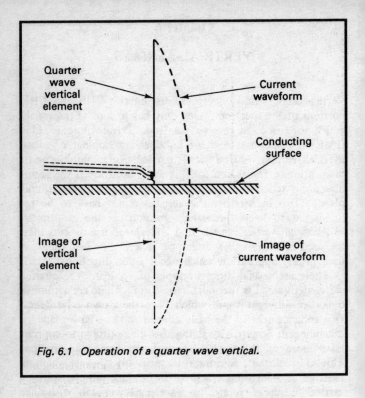

Fig. 6.1 *Operation of a quarter wave vertical.*

maximum. This gives the aerial a low feed impedance.

To enable the aerial to operate a ground plane is required. Ideally this is a perfectly conducting plane which serves to mirror the vertical section of the aerial.

In theory this plane extends out to infinity. However in practice the ground plane is normally simulated quite satisfactorily by a number of rods about a quarter wavelength long, extending out from the base as shown in Figure 6.2. This is normally quite adequate for the majority of applications where four radials normally suffice. Only rarely are any more used at VHF or UHF.

When space is at a premium it is possible to reduce the size of the radial system. This can be done as shown in Figure 6.3 by bending round the radials into the form of a circle. When

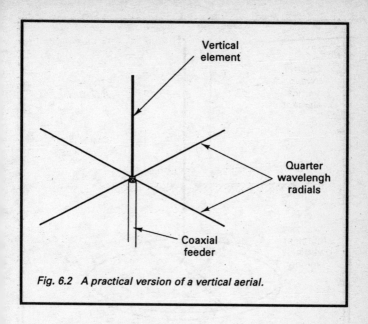

Fig. 6.2 A practical version of a vertical aerial.

this is done, the actual radial section L1 should be about 0.07 of a wavelength. The circumference of the circle should then be about 0.43 of a wavelength. This type of arrangement also has the advantage that it can be made to be more rugged than the conventional radials. However it does have the disadvantage that it has a much narrower bandwidth than an aerial with conventional radials and the feed impedance is low.

For mobile applications the car body metalwork acts as an ideal ground plane. This means there is no need for any radials and makes the vertical an ideal aerial for mobile use.

Matching

Matching a vertical to 50 Ω feeder can present some problems. In its basic form shown in Figure 6.2 the feed impedance of the aerial is about 20 Ω or less. There are a number of ways to overcome this. One solution which can be used is to use a folded vertical element similar to that used in a folded dipole. This will raise the impedance by a factor of four, making it more suitable for 50 or 75 Ω coax.

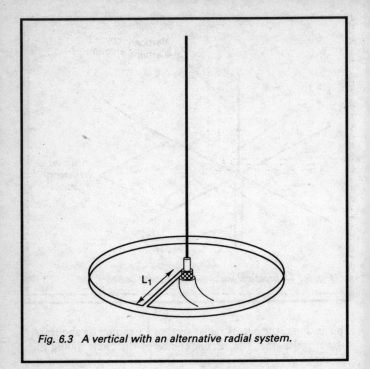

Fig. 6.3 A vertical with an alternative radial system.

Another solution which is often more convenient for the home constructor is to bend the radials downwards. This raises the feed impedance towards that of a dipole which the aerial would become if the radials were tilted completely downwards.

A third solution is to include an impedance matching element in the aerial. Normally this is in the form of a tapped coil which can be conveniently housed in the base of the aerial. This solution is more normally used in variants of the vertical where the feed impedance is too high.

Radiation Pattern
One of the major advantages of the vertical aerial is that it radiates equally in all directions around it. Also in the vertical plane the direction of maximum radiation is at right

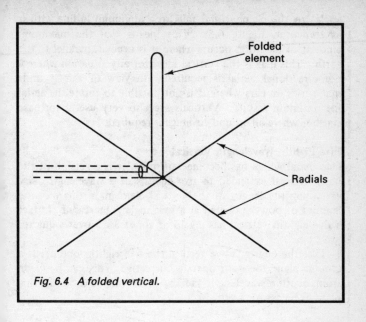

Fig. 6.4 A folded vertical.

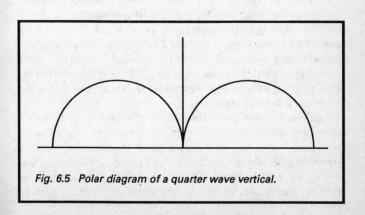

Fig. 6.5 Polar diagram of a quarter wave vertical.

angles to the element and falls to a minimum in line with it as shown in Figure 6.5. This means that the maximum amount of radiation occurs where it is needed, parallel to the earth. This makes the vertical ideal for any situation where a non-directional aerial is required. In view of this it finds many uses on cars where it is not possible to rotate the aerial for optimum results. Verticals are also very useful for base stations where all around coverage is required.

Five Eighths Wavelength Vertical

One aerial which has become very popular is a version of the basic vertical extended to five eighths of a wavelength. By extending the length of the vertical element in this way the amount of power radiated at a low angle is increased. In fact a five eighths vertical has a gain of about 3 dB over a quarter wave one.

Like the quarter wave vertical the five eighths one needs a ground plane for it to operate correctly. This can be made from quarter wavelength radials, or it can be a conducting plate like a car roof, etc.

J Aerials

One of the major drawbacks of the standard vertical aerial is the fact that it requires a set of radials or a ground plane if it is to operate correctly. This is not always convenient and it can sometimes be difficult to obtain the best results from a car. From a fixed location a set of radials increases the visual impact of the aerial and this may not be acceptable.

One solution to the problem is found in the form of the J aerial. In essence it is a form of Zepp (Zeppelin) aerial which found favour in the 1930s as an HF aerial. It consists of a half wave radiating element which is end fed using a quarter wave stub of open wire or 300 Ω balanced feeder used to match the impedance to the coaxial feeder.

Although there are a number of different ways in which this type of design can be implemented one of the most convenient is shown in Figure 6.6. It is quite easy to construct and gives good results. The main disadvantage is that it can be a little more difficult to adjust than some other forms. The reason for this is that impedance matching has to

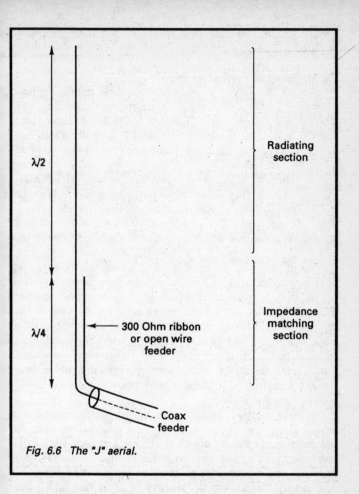

Fig. 6.6 The "J" aerial.

be accomplished by altering the trimming length of the stub.

The length of the half wave radiating stub can be determined using the same formula as used in calculating the length of a half wave dipole. The physical length of the balanced feeder will depend on the velocity factor of the feeder in use. For open wire feeder the velocity factor is nearly unity and the length will be very close to that of the free space quarter wavelength. If 300 ohm twin feeder is used then the length required will be shorter because its velocity factor is about 0.85.

Car Mounting of Vertical Aerials

In view of the very high usage of verticals in mobile applications on cars there is a very wide variety on the market. All interests are catered for. There are aerials for amateur radio and CB as well as the more professional uses like PMR. As might be expected there are a number of different ways of mounting these aerials.

The best way is to have a permanent mount. Whilst this is the most satisfactory it does mean putting a special hole in the car bodywork just for the aerial and often this is not acceptable. To overcome this problem a number of other mounts are available for cars which do not need any alterations to the car.

One of the most common is called a magnetic mount (Mag Mount for short). This form of mount has a base about five or six inches in diameter which includes a strong magnet. This enables the mount to be placed on the metalwork of the car and be held firmly in place. This form of mount has the advantage that it can be easily removed when the aerial is not required or the car is left unattended. When using a magnetic mount care should be taken to ensure that the rubber base remains free from dirt and grit otherwise the paintwork very soon becomes scratched.

Another method uses an attachment which fits to the gutter along the side of the car roof. Gutter mounts do not require any modifications to the car and they are a little more permanent than the magnetic mount. However they normally use a connector so that the aerial can be removed. This is very useful from the security point of view and it also allows for aerials to be changed if required, for example if the frequency band is changed.

Construction of a 70 cm Vertical

A quarter wave vertical aerial can be made very easily for a minimal cost. An example of a vertical for the 70 centimetre amateur band is shown in Figure 6.7. This type of aerial is likely to be used for FM operation which almost without

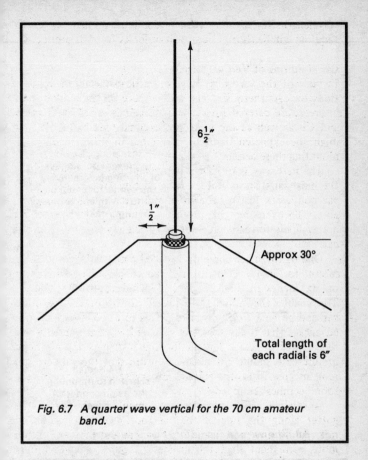

$6\frac{1}{2}''$

$\frac{1}{2}''$

Approx 30°

Total length of
each radial is 6″

*Fig. 6.7 A quarter wave vertical for the 70 cm amateur
band.*

exception uses vertical polarisation.

The aerial can be constructed out of 18 s.w.g. copper wire.
Whilst this gauge was used in the prototypes it is not particularly critical. Almost any suitable wire can be used although
thicker wire will be more rigid and will give a slightly wider
bandwidth. However the 18 s.w.g. wire is sufficiently rigid
for internal use.

The simplest way to construct the aerial is to simply
solder the wires cut to length directly onto the coax.
However other more ingenious methods can be used as well.

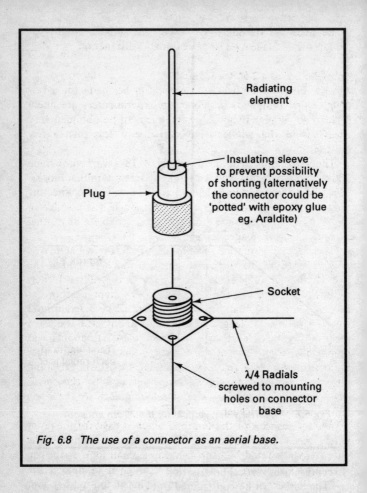

Radiating element

Insulating sleeve to prevent possibility of shorting (alternatively the connector could be 'potted' with epoxy glue eg. Araldite)

Plug

Socket

λ/4 Radials screwed to mounting holes on connector base

Fig. 6.8 The use of a connector as an aerial base.

One is to use a connector as the base of the aerial as shown in Figure 6.8. By using this a more rigid base is provided and the aerial can be easily disconnected when not in use.

The construction of the aerial is quite simple although a few notes may be helpful. The radials are bent slightly down as shown in the diagram. This has to be done to ensure a good match to the 50 Ω coax and final adjustments to the radials should bring the S.W.R. reading down to virtually 1:1 if it is to be used for transmitting. Using this aerial a number of contacts were made over some reasonable distances.

Construction of a 2 Metre J Aerial

A very simple yet effective J aerial can be made for a few pence using oddments which most experimenters are likely to have to hand. If not, then they can all be obtained very cheaply and the whole aerial should cost less than a few pounds.

The aerial only requires a length of 18 s.w.g. wire, some 300 Ω ribbon feeder and a couple of screw terminal blocks. The screw terminals provide an excellent way of connecting the different sections of the aerial. Although it is possible to solder the connections, this method enables any final adjustments to be made very easily.

The basic construction of the aerial is shown in Figure 6.9. A double section of the screw terminal block is used at the base of the aerial to connect the coax to the ribbon feeder. Here the wires from the coax should be kept as short as possible to ensure that the lengths given in the diagram hold true. The overall length of 300 Ω ribbon used was 16½ inches. This total length was needed because half an inch was prepared at each end for the connector block. One further point to note is that the centre conductor of the coax should ultimately connect to the radiating element of the aerial. The outer braid of the coax should connect to the open circuit wire of the feeder.

A single section of the terminal block is used for the point where the 300 Ω feeder and the wire element connect. The wire element should be bent round in a small loop at the top to enable some cord to be passed through it to hold it up.

The final aerial gave an S.W.R. reading of about 1.5:1 over most of the 2 metre band and very creditable results were obtained when it was used for transmitting and receiving. However it may be necessary for a few minor adjustments to be made to optimise the performance for the particular materials used. In this way the minimum S.W.R. reading can be obtained once the aerial is built.

To finish the aerial it can be housed in some plastic waste pipe. The white poly-propylene variety is the best as it has

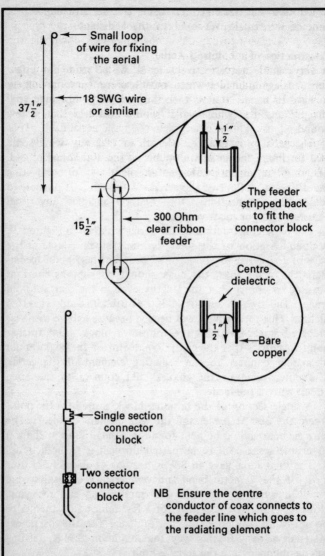

Small loop of wire for fixing the aerial

18 SWG wire or similar

$37\frac{1}{2}''$

$15\frac{1}{2}''$

$\frac{1}{2}''$

The feeder stripped back to fit the connector block

300 Ohm clear ribbon feeder

Centre dielectric

$\frac{1}{2}''$

Bare copper

Single section connector block

Two section connector block

NB Ensure the centre conductor of coax connects to the feeder line which goes to the radiating element

Fig. 6.9 The 2 metre J aerial.

70

been found that some of the p.v.c. varieties actually absorb some of the signal. When fitting the aerial into the pipe it may be necessary to cut the connecting block down slightly so that it easily slides into the pipe.

The top of the pipe can be sealed with a rubber stopper. This can be obtained from a suitable home wine making or brewing shop. If the aerial is to be housed in a pipe any final adjustments should be made with it in situ.

The pipe should be longer than the basic aerial itself. This extra length is needed at the base so that any metalwork used for fixing the aerial will be below the 300 Ω feeder and will not affect the performance of the aerial.

Chapter 7

WIDEBAND AERIALS

All the aerials which have been described so far have been able to cover only a comparatively small band of frequencies. For example an aerial designed for VHF FM use will only be able to operate over the range 88 to 108 MHz and in order to cover the full band, performance at either end of the band may have to be sacrificed a little. Other aerials may be designed to cover two or possibly three bands by using tuned circuits to isolate different parts of the aerial so that a number of different resonances are achieved. But even so it will not operate properly between the bands. In fact most aerials will only be able to operate over frequency ranges which correspond to a few percent of the operating frequency.

Fortunately some specialized types of aerial are able to operate over a very wide band of frequencies. Unlike other aerials which cover a single band or possibly several bands their performance will remain substantially the same over a range of frequencies covering a span of 2:1 or possibly even more. Wideband aerials like these are important for a number of different applications. One possible use is when an aerial is used in conjunction with a scanner. As the scanner will be able to cover a very wide range of frequencies very quickly it is not convenient to have a wide range of aerials which have to be switched. The only viable solution is to use a proper wideband aerial.

The Discone
This type of aerial must be the most popular type of wideband aerial used by scanner enthusiasts. It is almost omni-directional and it can operate over a frequency range of up to 10:1 in certain instances. In addition to this it offers a low angle of radiation which is particularly important at VHF and UHF. However it must be said that the angle of radiation does increase at the top of the frequency range.

The discone derives its name from the distinctive shape which is shown in Figure 7.1. From this diagram it can be

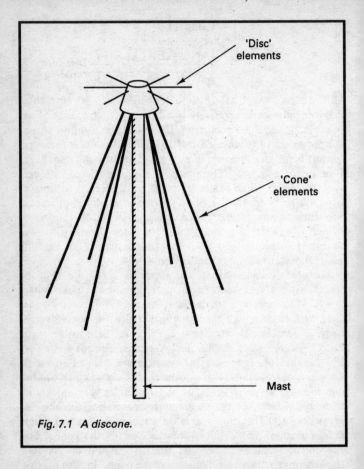

Fig. 7.1 A discone.

seen that the aerial basically consists of a disc and a cone. The disc section is insulated from the cone by a block of material which also acts as a spacer keeping the two sections a fixed distance apart. In fact this distance is one of the factors which determines the overall frequency range of the aerial.

When designing a discone the length of the cone elements should be approximately a quarter wavelength at the minimum operating frequency. Then it is found that for the flattest response the angle of the elements to the vertical should be

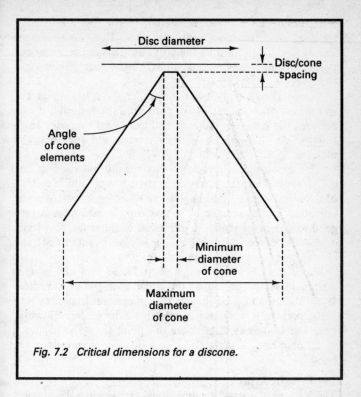

Fig. 7.2 Critical dimensions for a discone.

between 25 and 45 degrees. Having decided upon this the disc elements should be made to have an overall length of about 0.7 of that of the diameter of the base of the cone. The spacing between the cone and the disc should be about a quarter of the minimum diameter of the cone. In turn making the minimum diameter of the cone small will increase the upper frequency limit of the aerial.

Operation
The actual operation of a discone is quite complicated, but it is possible to visualize it in a simple qualitative manner. First the elements which form the disc and cone tend to electrically simulate a complete surface from which the energy is radiated. Although the number of elements which are used is not critical,

it is found that a better simulation of the disc and cone is achieved when more elements are used. However additional elements will add both to the cost and the wind resistance of the aerial and therefore it is normal to use about six or eight elements.

In operation energy from the feeder meets the aerial and spreads over the surface of the cone until the vertical distance between the point on the cone and the disc is a quarter wavelength. At this point resonance is seen and the energy is radiated.

The signal which is radiated is vertically polarized as one might expect and the radiation pattern is very similar to that of a vertical dipole. Although some variation is seen over the operating band particularly at the top, it maintains a very good low angle of radiation over most of the range. Typically one would expect virtually no change over a range of 5:1 and above this a slight increase in the angle.

From the circuit viewpoint it is found that the current maximum is at the top of the aerial as might be expected. It is also found that below the minimum frequency the aerial presents a very bad mismatch to the feeder. However once the frequency rises above this point then a good match to 50 ohm coax is maintained over virtually the whole of the band.

Log Periodic Array

The log periodic array is a directional aerial unlike the discone. However it is normally capable of operating over a frequency range of about 2:1. It has many similarities to the more familiar Yagi because it exhibits a useful amount of forward gain and has a significant front to back ratio. In addition to this the radiation pattern stays broadly the same over the whole of the operating band as do parameters like the radiation resistance and the standing wave ratio. However it offers less gain for its size than does the more conventional Yagi. Accordingly log periodic arrays tend to be used only in some specialized applications and they are often quite large.

Operation of Log Periodic Arrays

There are several basic forms of the log periodic array. However the one which has gained the most popularity is the log

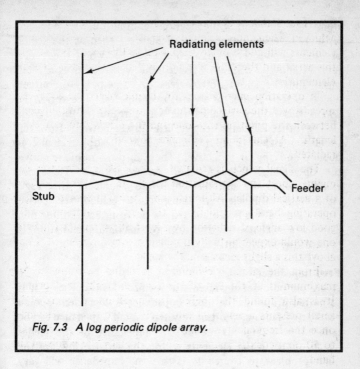

Fig. 7.3 A log periodic dipole array.

periodic dipole array which is shown in Figure 7.3. Essentially it consists of a number of dipole elements having different lengths and different spacings. Unlike the Yagi each element is driven as shown and the feeder is terminated in a stub to ensure a good match. It can also be seen that the lengths of the elements increase away from the feed point as do the inter-element spacings. It is because of these changing dimensions that the log periodic exhibits its wide bandwidth.

The operation of a log periodic can be explained in a fairly simple qualitative manner. From the diagram it can be seen that the polarity of the feeder is reversed between successive elements. For the sake of the explanation imagine a signal is applied to the aerial somewhere around the middle of its operating range. When the signal meets the first few elements it will be found that they are spaced quite close together in terms of the operating wavelength. This means that the fields from these elements will cancel one another out as the feeder sense is reversed between the elements. Then as the signal progresses down the aerial a point is reached where the feeder reversal and the distance between the elements gives a total phase shift of about 360 degrees. At this point the effect which is seen is that of two phased dipoles. The region in which this occurs is called the active region of the aerial.

The other elements receive little direct power. However the larger elements are resonant below the operational frequency and appear inductive. Those in front resonate above the operational frequency and are capacitive. These are exactly the same criteria which are found in the Yagi. Accordingly the element immediately behind the active region acts as a reflector and those in front act as directors. This means that the direction of maximum radiation is towards the feed point.

Feed Impedance

A log periodic aerial presents a number of difficulties if it is to be fed properly. Its input impedance is dependent upon a number of factors. Fortunately the overall impedance can be tailored to a large degree by the impedance of the feeder which connects the elements within the aerial. However the main problem to overcome is that the impedance will vary according to the frequency in use. To a large extent this can be compensated by making the longer elements out of a larger diameter rod. Even so the final feed impedance does not normally match a convenient 50 ohms on its own. It is normal for some further form of impedance matching to have to be used. This may be in the form of a stub or even a transformer. The actual method employed will depend to a large degree on the application of the aerial and its frequency range.

Chapter 8

AERIAL MEASUREMENTS

Testing of aerial systems can sometimes involve the use of equipment which is not normally present in the average electronic enthusiast's house. Some of these items can be expensive, especially if rigorous and accurate measurements are to be made. Unfortunately items like a standard test meter are really only useful for the basic continuity and insulation measurements which will tell if the connections have been made correctly. However if the measurements to be made do not need to be very accurate, and a little improvisation can be used, then it is possible to perform enough tests to ensure that the aerial is operating to the best of its ability. In order to do this items like a dip meter or a standing wave ratio meter can form the basic stock of equipment which is used.

What is a Dip Meter?
Dip meters are called a variety of different names depending upon the type of amplifying device used in them. Early meters using valves were called grid dip oscillators (g.d.o.) whereas later meters using FETs altered the name slightly to gate dip oscillator. However they may even be called FET dip oscillators and there may be other names as well for ordinary bipolar transistor meters. But whatever they are called they are essentially the same piece of equipment.

A dip meter or dip oscillator is an instrument which contains an oscillator which can be tuned over a wide range of frequencies. Generally there are several ranges which can be chosen by the use of external plug-in coils like that shown in Figure 8.1. Their operation depends upon the fact that when a tank or tuned circuit of an oscillator is placed close to another resonant circuit the oscillator current will drop when tuned to the resonant frequency of the external circuit. By doing this it is possible to check the resonant frequency of almost any tuned circuit regardless of whether it is on a circuit board or whether it forms part of an aerial. Thus a dip

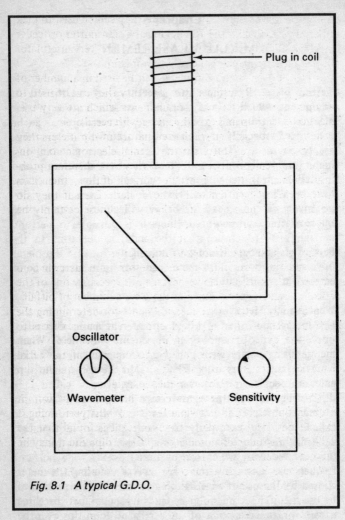

Fig. 8.1 A typical G.D.O.

oscillator is essentially a form of calibrated variable frequency oscillator in which it is possible to monitor the oscillator current.

Apart from acting as an oscillator, most meters have the facility to turn the oscillator off so that they can be used as an absorption wavemeter. In this mode they can be used to pick up strong signals like the RF field near a transmitter or feeder carrying RF power. In this form they are very useful for checking the frequency band of a transmission.

It can be seen that a dip meter can be used in a number of different ways. By using a little ingenuity they can be used to perform a great variety of measurements which are very useful when setting up and experimenting with aerials.

In view of the rather specialized nature of dip meters they are not always available from the normal electronic component and equipment stockists. In cases where there are problems in locating them from the normal outlets, then it is worth trying a local amateur radio dealer. Even if they do not have one themselves then they will almost certainly be able to advise where to obtain one.

Measuring an Aerial's Resonant Frequency

This is probably the most obvious use for a dip meter in connection with an aerial. However it is not necessarily one of the easiest measurement to make as there are a number of pitfalls.

In common with other measurements for determining the resonant frequency of a tuned circuit, the basic idea is to couple the coil of the meter to the circuit under test. When the meter is tuned to the resonant frequency of the aerial then the meter current will dip. The centre of the dip indicates the resonant frequency of the aerial.

When performing this measurement it is best to perform it at the aerial itself and not via a feeder. Whilst performing it via a feeder may seem perfectly in order it is found that the feeder will introduce a number of spurious dips and it may be difficult to identify the correct response.

When checking the aerial some way of coupling the meter to the aerial must be found. For an aerial in the HF section of the spectrum it is possible to take a loop of two or three turns from the feed point of the aerial and loop this over the coil of the dip meter. It may even be possible to use this method having a single turn loop at the low end of the VHF portion of the spectrum, but as the frequency rises then it may introduce some inaccuracies. The best way, if sufficient coupling can be obtained, is to short out the feed point and

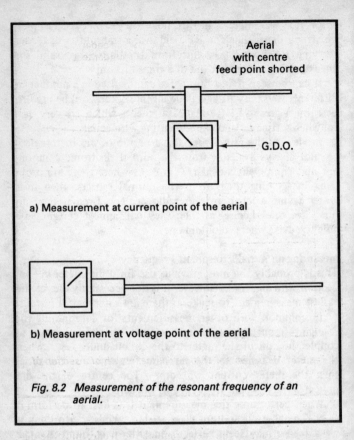

a) Measurement at current point of the aerial

b) Measurement at voltage point of the aerial

Fig. 8.2 Measurement of the resonant frequency of an aerial.

place the coil as close as possible to the aerial as shown in Figure 8.2. It will be found that the best dip using the method of Figure 8.2(a) is at a current maximum, i.e. at the feed point of most aerials. If the method of Figure 8.2(b) is used then the best dip will be obtained at a point of voltage maximum. This can always be found at the end of an aerial.

Measuring the Electrical Length of a Feeder
A dip meter provides an easy method of measuring the electrical length of a piece of feeder. A knowledge of this length can be of value in a number of applications especially if the

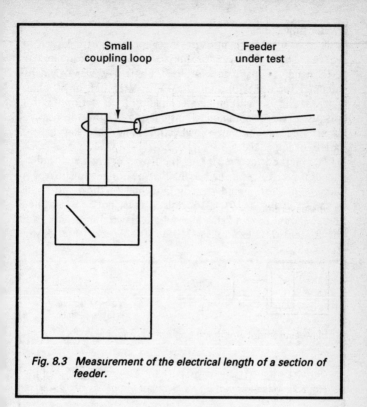

Fig. 8.3   Measurement of the electrical length of a section of feeder.

aerial installation is used for transmitting.

In order to make the measurement the feeder must be disconnected from the aerial and left open circuit. The other end should then be coupled to the dip meter as shown in Figure 8.3. Then with the meter in its oscillator mode it should be tuned from its lowest frequency upwards until a dip is noted. This frequency should be noted as it is the primary resonant frequency. However it is wise to check this by tuning further up in frequency to the next few dips. These are harmonics of the fundamental resonance and they should be at multiples of the frequency of the first dip. If all is correct then the frequency of the first dip corresponds to a quarter wavelength.

Feeder Impedance

It is also possible to measure the impedance of a length of feeder. This can be very useful if a length of unknown coax is to hand. Usually it will be 75 ohms if it was originally intended for use with domestic TV or VHF FM, or 50 ohms if it was for use with an amateur radio or CB station, or if it was used for a commercial installation. However coax is often used in computer installations and this can have a variety of impedances.

The method involves taking the length of coax and finding the dip for its resonance as in the measurement above. A variable resistor should then be attached to the remote end as shown in Figure 8.4. This resistor must not be wirewound and it should have a value above the expected impedance for the feeder. For example a 250 or 500 ohm variable resistor

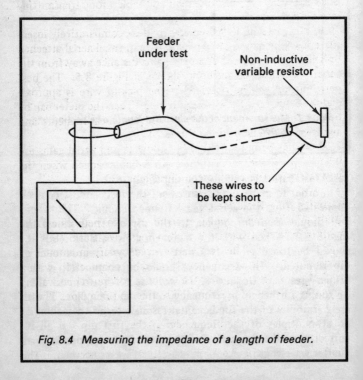

Fig. 8.4 Measuring the impedance of a length of feeder.

would be suitable for most applications. In order to ensure the accuracy of the measurement the connections to the variable resistor should be as short as possible. If they are too long then there is the possibility that some stray reactance will be added into the circuit and this could alter the readings.

At this point the resistor should be varied until the dip on the meter disappears. The value of the resistor then corresponds to the characteristic impedance of the feeder. It should then be carefully removed and its resistance measured using a standard multimeter.

Using a Dip Meter as a Field Strength Meter

Apart from being used in its oscillator mode a dip meter can also find a number of uses in its wavemeter mode. For this it is used to pick up the signal transmitted from the aerial and so this is really a measurement suitable for transmitting installations.

As the meter in its wavemeter mode is comparatively insensitive it will need to have a pickup wire or small aerial attached to it if it is to be placed at a reasonable distance away from the aerial. This can be set up as shown in Figure 8.5. The best performance will be obtained if the pickup wire is approximately a quarter of a wavelength long. Then the meter can be tuned to the correct frequency and the measurements and adjustments can be made to the aerial.

It should be noted that if high powers and aerial gains are involved then the aerial should not be approached when the power is on as this can present a health hazard.

Standing Wave Ratio Meters

Another instrument which can be used to help assess the performance of an aerial is a Standing Wave Ratio (S.W.R.) Bridge. In view of the fact that it needs a certain amount of power to drive it, it is generally used in conjunction with a transmitter. It measures the amount of power travelling down the feeder away from the source and compares it with any reflected power. From this it is able to give a reading of the S.W.R. that exists in the feeder.

The S.W.R. that exists in a feeder is very important for a number of reasons where transmitters are concerned. The

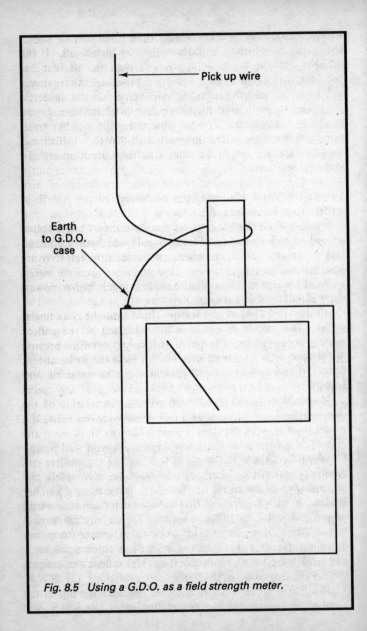

Fig. 8.5 Using a G.D.O. as a field strength meter.

first is that if the S.W.R. is high then there will be points where the current and voltage reach very high levels. If the transmitter is running at high power then the current can become sufficiently high to cause local heating. Alternatively at the voltage peaks there is the possibility that the dielectric can break down. Both of these possibilities can damage the coax. In addition to this most transmitters do not like operating in conditions where there is a high S.W.R. In fact it is possible for damage to be caused to the output stage. To prevent this most transmitters have protection circuitry which reduces the output power under conditions of high levels of S.W.R. Accordingly a knowledge of the S.W.R. in the feeder is very important.

The more simple meters are normally not very complicated in terms of the number of components which they contain, and it is quite easy to build a simple one, although they are also not too expensive to buy. However more accurate meters or ones which are capable of handling much higher powers are naturally more expensive.

In use an S.W.R. Bridge will be fitted into the coax line as shown in Figure 8.6, and it will be located at the end of the feeder away from the aerial. It is very convenient because it can be left in circuit all the time. This is useful because it means that any major aerial problems can be detected very quickly. In addition to this the bandwidth of any aerial system is limited and the S.W.R. will rise either side of the centre frequency. If a transmitter is likely to be used on a number of frequencies then it is necessary to know what the S.W.R. is on the new frequency before applying full power.

Whilst an indication of the S.W.R. at the transmitter end of the feeder is very useful it does not give a complete picture about the operation of the aerial. There are a number of reasons for this. One is that a poor feeder can hide a high level of S.W.R. The reason for this is that any feeder will have a certain amount of loss. This will attenuate the power travelling towards the aerial as well as any power which is reflected back. Both of these effects will reduce the amount of reflected power seen by the meter, making the S.W.R. reading seem better than it really is. In fact the higher the level of attenuation in the feeder the better the S.W.R. will

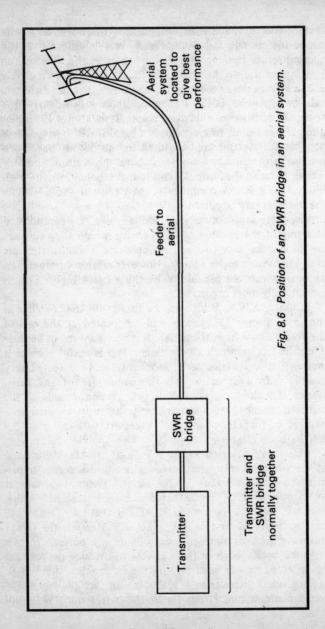

Aerial system located to give best performance

Feeder to aerial

SWR bridge

Transmitter

Transmitter and SWR bridge normally together

Fig. 8.6 Position of an SWR bridge in an aerial system.

seem. Thus it is quite possible for an aerial to reflect a large proportion of its power, but seem to be operating quite satisfactorily if the feeder loss is high.

Measuring Feeder Loss

The fact that the S.W.R. reading is altered in this way can be used as the basis of a simple method to determine the actual feeder loss. It is very convenient because the feeder can be left in situ and all the measurements are performed at one end. All that needs doing at the far end is for the load or aerial to be replaced by a complete short or open circuit so that all the power is reflected. Once this is done a simple measurement of the S.W.R. is performed. Then using the table of values contained in Figure 8.7, it is possible to determine the actual loss.

Fig. 8.7   Table of S.W.R. Against Loss for a Feeder Terminated in a Complete Short or Open Circuit

S.W.R.	Feeder Loss (dB)
1.02:1	20
1.05:1	16
1.10:1	13
1.20:1	10
1.4:1	7.5
1.6:1	6
1.8:1	5
2.0:1	4.5
2.5:1	3.5
3:1	3
4:1	2
5:1	1.75
6:1	1.5
10:1	0.75
15:1	0.6
20:1	0.4

Although this method of measuring feeder loss is very convenient in many respects there are a number of points which need to be noted if it is to be used. The first is that the signal generator or transmitter must be capable of operating with a high level of S.W.R. without any fear of damage. In addition to this the minimum level of power must be used. This will prevent any damage to the feeder caused by the peaks of voltage and current associated with a high S.W.R. It is also worth noting that the termination must be as good as possible. If it is a short circuit then the wire making the connection must be as short as possible, especially for frequencies above 30 MHz. The reason for this is that any stray inductance from the wire will have some reactance which may distort the readings. Another point to remember is that the loss of a feeder will rise quite rapidly with frequency, and it is necessary to make the readings at the frequency of operation.

Chapter 9

PRACTICAL ASPECTS

Apart from knowing how aerials function and how to design or build them, it is equally important to know how to fit them up. The knack of knowing the best place to mount the aerial is obviously very important. It is also vital to know how to fix the aerial up properly so that it does not fall down and injure someone. Then it is very useful to be able to know all the precautions to take to prevent the aerial system as a whole deteriorating because of the weather.

Inside or Out

It is often far more convenient to have aerials mounted inside the house. It can sometimes be quite unsightly to have aerials on the skyline. In addition to this the aerials are protected from the winds and rain. This may be a distinct consideration for a home-made aerial which may not be able to withstand the rigours of being placed outside. Furthermore it is often a lot easier to put an aerial up in the loft rather than having to climb up to a suitable point on the outside of the house for the aerial, with all the attendant dangers and difficulties.

Unfortunately an aerial will always perform better if it is outside the house. The roof is not in the way of the incoming signals. There are less objects around it to de-tune the aerial and so forth. Unfortunately it is difficult to put a figure on the amount of loss caused by mounting an aerial inside. It will vary tremendously from one situation to another. Then it will also be dependent upon the frequency in use. But as a rough guide the loss in the VHF and UHF portions of the spectrum is unlikely to be less than 6 dB and probably more.

In areas of strong reception this may not be a problem, but in areas where the signal is at all marginal an external aerial is almost a necessity. It could be the difference between a crystal clear TV picture and one which has an annoying amount of "grass" or noise on it. It could be the difference between a good FM hi-fi signal and one which has a high level of background noise. Then for radio amateurs and listeners it could be the difference between a successful station and one which is not.

Choosing the Best Spot

The choice of the best position for the aerial is particularly important. A good aerial can have its performance degraded purely by its position. Conversely the best can be made of an aerial by putting it in the optimum position.

The aerial should have a good "view" in the direction it is meant to beam. For a TV or VHF FM broadcast aerial there should be no large objects between the aerial and the transmitter site. Large buildings with all their associated metalwork and wiring will significantly attenuate the signal. Even trees can have an effect especially if they are wet. This means that if it is possible it is best to choose a site which avoids them. It might be that one chimney stack has a better view than another.

The aerial should be as high as possible. Added height will help the aerial to clear many of the obstructions which could reduce the signal strength.

Apart from enabling the aerial to clear nearby obstructions an increase in height will give signal improvements over long paths because the horizon is extended. Often a doubling in height can bring a gain of 3 dB or possibly more.

As with any rule there is always an exception and the maximum height may not always give the best signal. Sometimes there can be an advantage in using a house or other obstruction to screen the aerial from sources of interference. One instance of this may be with TV or VHF FM aerials which might pick up car ignition interference from a nearby road. If the house can be used to help screen the interference and not the wanted signal the reception can be improved. This may be one instance when increasing the height of the aerial does not necessarily improve all aspects of reception.

Another factor worth bearing in mind when positioning the aerial is that any metal objects, even if they are not in the line of the aerial could tend to de-tune it if they are too close. This could reduce the efficiency of the aerial and so reduce the signal.

Indoor Aerials

Often an aerial will have to be mounted internally. In this case the positioning of the aerial is still very important. Many of the metallic objects which can impair the performance of an aerial will not be as obvious. There will be nearby objects which can de-tune the aerial and others can screen it from the wanted signal.

Most indoor aerials will be mounted in the roof space. Here the major item of metalwork will be the water tank. This is large and obvious, but wiring for lighting on the floor below is likely to run between the boards and can de-tune the aerial if it is left on the floor or close to it. Another major item of metalwork is the metal chimney liner which is found in many houses these days. This too can have a large effect on signals.

Ideally the aerial should be mounted about half way between the roof and the floor. It should also be mounted clear of any other metallic objects. This should minimise any de-tuning effects. In addition to this it should be positioned so that it is not directed at any metal objects or even close to them.

Choosing an Aerial

There is a very wide variety of aerials which are available ready built. TV and VHF FM radio aerials are readily available from many TV or electronics component retailers. Aerials for other purposes such as amateur radio are available from specialist outlets.

Home-built aerials are ideal for indoor use, experimentation and for specialist applications. However commercially built ones offer good value and are designed to withstand the rigours of the weather. They are generally built out of aluminium tubing and are fairly rugged.

When choosing a TV aerial it is very important to select one for the correct frequency band. As the TV channels cover such a wide band of frequencies, aerials are split into a number of different groups. In fact television broadcasts within a particular area will fall within one of these groups. It is therefore important to choose the correct aerial.

In most of Europe six groups are in use. The local TV or aerial supplier should be able to advise which group is required for a particular area.

Fig.9.1   UHF TV Aerial Groups

Group	Channel Numbers
A	21 – 34
B	39 – 53
C/D	48 – 68
E	39 – 68
K	21 – 48
W	21 – 68

Virtually all television aerials are Yagis. This means that aerials having a wider bandwidth will have less gain than narrow band ones. To achieve the same gain a wide band aerial will need to have more elements and will be larger than one covering a small bandwidth.

Sealing the Feeder

The loss in a feeder will rise dramatically if moisture enters it. However most aerials are installed outside and they are open to the elements. Eventually moisture will enter the coax even if there is a covered connection box on the aerial. This will result in a slow but sure degradation in the performance of the whole system.

In order to prevent this happening it is necessary to seal the end of the coax. The silicone rubber bath sealants can be used for this. The whole of the end of the cable should be coated in this to make a good water-tight seal.

Multiple Antennas on a Mast

It is quite in order to put more than one antenna on a mast. For example, it may be necessary to have a TV and an FM aerial together or possibly two beams for different amateur bands. However to ensure that the optimum performance is obtained and one aerial does not degrade the performance of the other, it is necessary to have the right spacing.

Generally the aerial for the higher frequency band is placed at the top. This places less strain on the mast as the smaller aerial will be at the top. As a rough rule of thumb the minimum spacing between the two aerials should be half the length of the boom of the top aerial.

If it is possible to achieve a wider spacing than this better results can be achieved. It has been previously shown that the impedance of an aerial varies with its height above ground. In the case of two stacked aerials the lower one appears like ground to the higher one. At points half a wavelength or a multiple of a half wavelength above ground the impedance passes through its nominal or free space value. This means that the aerial impedance will be correct at this spacing.

In addition to this the lower aerial will act as a reflector or ground plane for the upper one. Again at multiples of a half wavelength the effect is such that a low angle of radiation is achieved. It is worth noting that for odd multiples of a quarter wavelength there is a considerable amount of high angle radiation.

Aligning the Aerial

When an aerial is erected it must be aligned in the direction of the transmitter. The actual direction can be determined using a map or the general direction can be ascertained from any other similar aerials in the vicinity.

Once in position the aerial may require some adjustment to obtain the optimum signal. In most cases this will mean adjusting it for the strongest signal. This may not necessarily be in the exact direction of the transmitter. Obstructions like tall buildings or hills can mean that the aerial needs to be offset from the estimated direction.

The alignment of television aerials is generally fairly easy. The strongest signal usually corresponds to the best picture. However on occasions the aerial may need to be offset from this position to reduce any "ghosting". This is caused by reflections which are picked up. As they arrive a fraction of a second later than the main signal they cause a second image slightly offset from the main one. When this occurs the position of the aerial will be a compromise between the minimum ghost signal and the maximum wanted one. Often the problem can be reduced by having a higher gain aerial with more directivity.

A number of problems can also occur when aligning aerials for VHF FM radio use. Again the aerial should be positioned to give the maximum signal strength. This will correspond to a reduction in background hiss on the signal. This noise will be far more apparent on stereo than on mono. If the noise cannot be reduced sufficiently then a better location may be required for the aerial, or a high gain aerial may be needed.

On occasions an unusual form of hiss or warble may be heard on both mono and stereo. This may mean the signal is too strong and the inclusion of an attenuator in the feeder can eliminate the effect. Attenuators can be bought from most aerial or components stockists.

If a background warbling is found only in stereo then it is likely to result from interference from other stations. To reduce this the aerial can be rotated so that the signal from the offending station is reduced. Generally this is done by finding a null in the response of the aerial for the offending station, but keeping the wanted station on the main lobe of the aerial. Alternatively a larger more directive aerial may be needed.

Another problem which can occur is that high frequency sounds especially can be distorted. This results from the signal being reflected in a similar way to television ghosting. If this occurs the aerial should be rotated to minimise this effect.

Safety

When any aerial system is fitted up care and thought must be exercised to ensure that it is perfectly safe. Home-built aerials are particularly at risk, and if there is any doubt they should not be erected outside. In addition to this commercially-made aerials should be fitted properly. The weather will soon find any weakness in the aerial itself or the fitting, so it is not worth taking any short cuts. It is better to be safe than sorry!

It is also wise to ensure that in the event of the aerial falling down, there is no possibility of it touching any power lines. If this happens the aerial can become live. This is obviously very dangerous, and people have been killed in the past when this has happened.

Finally it is necessary to ensure that the erection of an aerial does not require planning permission, and that it does not infringe any local regulations governing the erection of aerials. Many modern housing estates and flats have clauses written into their contracts forbidding even small aerials to be installed. It is therefore wise to check first.

Appendix

FREQUENCIES AND CHANNELS

UK Broadcast Bands above 30 MHz

Band	Frequency Range (MHz)	Channel Numbers	Uses
1	41 – 68	1 – 5	405 line TV (these transmissions have now been discontinued in the UK and these bands have been released for other services)
2	88 – 108	–	FM Radio
3	174 – 216	6 – 13	405 line TV (see note for band 1)
4	470 – 582	21 – 34	625 line TV
5	614 – 854	39 – 68	625 line TV

UK Television Channel Frequencies

Channel No.	Vision Carrier Frequency	Sound Carrier Frequency
21	471.25	477.25
22	479.25	485.25
23	487.25	493.25
24	495.25	501.25
25	503.25	509.25
26	511.25	517.25
27	519.25	525.25
28	527.25	533.25
29	535.25	541.25
30	543.25	549.25
31	551.25	557.25

Channel No.	Vision Carrier Frequency	Sound Carrier Frequency
32	559.25	565.25
33	567.25	573.25
34	575.25	581.25
39	615.25	621.25
40	623.25	629.25
41	631.25	637.25
42	639.25	645.25
43	647.25	653.25
44	655.25	661.25
45	663.25	669.25
46	671.25	677.25
47	679.25	685.25
48	687.25	693.25
49	695.25	701.25
50	703.25	709.25
51	711.25	717.25
52	719.25	725.25
53	727.25	733.25
54	735.25	741.25
55	743.25	749.25
56	751.25	757.25
57	759.25	765.25
58	767.25	773.25
59	775.25	781.25
60	783.25	789.25
61	791.25	797.25
62	799.25	805.25
63	807.25	813.25
64	815.25	821.25
65	823.25	829.25
66	831.25	837.25
67	839.25	845.25
68	847.25	853.25

All frequencies are in MHz

UK Amateur Bands in the VHF and UHF Spectrum

Frequency Limits (MHz)		Approx. Wavelength
50.00	52.00	6 Metres
70.00	70.50	4 Metres
144.00	146.00	2 Metres
430.00	440.00	70 cms
1240.00	1325.00	23 cms
2310.00	2450.00	13 cms

UK 934 MHz Citizen's Band Frequencies

Channel	Frequency
1	934.025
2	934.075
3	934.125
4	934.175
5	934.225
6	934.275
7	934.325
8	934.375
9	934.425
10	934.475
11	934.525
12	934.575
13	934.625
14	934.675
15	934.725
16	934.775
17	934.825
18	934.875
19	934.925
20	934.975

Index